To

THE SATURDAY BOOK

TWELFTH YEAR

THIS TWELFTH ANNUAL ISSUE
OF THE SATURDAY BOOK
HAS BEEN DESIGNED BY
LAURENCE SCARFE
EDWIN SMITH AND
THE EDITOR

Twelfth   *Issue of*

The
SATURDAY BOOK

❀ *Founded by Leonard Russell* ❀

Edited by John Hadfield

PUBLISHED BY THE MACMILLAN COMPANY

THIS TWELFTH ANNUAL ISSUE OF THE SATURDAY BOOK is made and printed in Great Britain at the Mayflower Press (of Plymouth) at Watford by William Brendon and Son, Ltd. The type has been set at the Gainsborough Press, St. Albans, by Fisher, Knight and Company, Ltd. The four-colour plates were engraved and printed by the Grout Engraving Company, Ltd., at Bromley. The book was bound by Dow and Lester, Ltd., at Luton.

PUBLISHED IN 1952

The shell roundel on the wrapper and the wool-picture on the title-page are reproduced by courtesy of the Lady Christina Gathorne-Hardy and the Hon. Hugh Gathorne-Hardy. The Georgian wallpaper reproduced on the wrapper was lent by Messrs Coles of Mortimer Street. The poem by W. H. Davies on page 84 is reprinted by permission of Messrs Jonathan Cape, Ltd.

THE CONTENTS

SATURDAY BOOK STORIES

★

THE 'TWENTIES

Illustrations by Edward Ardizzone
Eric Fitch Daglish, Susan Einzig, Frederick Exell
Robert Gibbings, Philip Gough, Anthony Gilbert,
Miles Hadfield, Diana Mason, Sarah Nechamkin
Brian Robb, Laurence Scarfe, Ronald Searle
and Edwin Smith

P.S. As we were going to press we realized that this issue contained nothing about Crime, which our revered Founder, in his first issue, twelve years since, postulated as a necessary ingredient in the book. Shamefacedly, and as a manifest fill-up, we have squeezed in this Elizabethan woodcut of that cobwebby whodunit, the murder of Thomas Arden of Feversham, in February, 1550–1, by Black Will and Shakbag, to the order of Mistress Arden and her paramour, Mosbie.

INTRODUCTION

WE WERE house-hunting. We were driving between June-scented hedgerows down a lane in Buckinghamshire, blissfully imagining ourselves to be the squire of a gracious Jacobean manor or a Capability Brown landskip, when we were brought up against reality—and the Grendon Underwood bus—by the thought that we had to write, that very evening, the Introduction to *The Saturday Book*.

House-hunting, if one indulges in it as a hobby rather than a dire necessity, transports one all too easily into cloud-cuckoo-land. One wanders irresponsibly from Priory to Park, from Olde Forge to New Hall (which is always the oldest house in the village), from dream house to dream house. One becomes bewitched by a derelict windmill or a castle in ruins, and brushes lightly aside the necessity of building licences or the fact that one's El Dorado is fourteen miles from the railway station. One strolls proprietorially through Palladian halls whose Augustan echoes discreetly suppress the existence of eighteen bedrooms and dry rot in the roof.

In such a state of bemusement it was unnerving to be brought up against the harsh realities of Editorship. As it happens, we had, until then, regarded our Editorship itself as a kind of cloud-cuckoo-land. We had never *really* believed in the telephone call when Leonard Russell asked us to adopt his child—as precocious, prodigious, white-headed a boy as any Hampdenshire Wonder.

Now, it seemed, our sojourn in moonshine was over. We had to face the cold dawn of writing an Introduction. We had, of course, read all the Introductions which our Founder and Benefactor had written for the previous eleven volumes; but in all candour we must say that they told us very little about the mysteries of Editorship, except, per-haps, that Leonard Russell worked on the principle of only putting into the book the things he liked. We had to admit that we had worked on precisely the same principle ourselves; but that was not very clever or very difficult. The only positive claim we could make was that we had crammed in rather more pictures and more pages than ever before (and we weren't quite sure how enthusiastically our publishers were going to react to that).

So we were at our wit's end to decide what we should write about when we knocked at the door of the half-timbered Elizabethan farm-house we had come to view. It was, needless to say, exactly the house we had always wanted—a wealth of oak beams, ingle-nooks, latticed windows, Tudor fireplaces. (We are, you must realize, agent-prone.)

7

'And now,' said the owner, as we climbed the spiral staircase, whose massive octagonal newels sprouted into flamboyant acorn heads of old oak, 'you must see the Shakespeare Room.' Her remark meant little to us until we stood in a timber-studded attic, with a curious oval window. Then the owner added casually, as though we must know it already: 'This is the room where Shakespeare wrote *A Midsummer Night's Dream.*'

At this point we supposed, naturally, that we too were in a dream. But apparently the owner was not. The house in which we stood, so she told us, used to be an inn, on the road from Stratford to London, and John Aubrey had recorded in the seventeenth century a conversation with a local worthy who himself remembered Master Shakespeare putting up for the night and retiring early to his attic room to get on with his new play.

'We are living in history,' we said to ourselves. 'The present is sheer illusion.' True, the next room we went into contained h. and c. and all mod. con., but, after all, it was an Elizabethan, Sir John Harington, who invented the water closet, as one can prove by looking at his design in *The Metamorphosis of Ajax*, 1596, which we reproduce at the foot of this page.

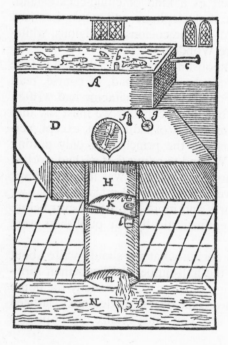

A priuie in perfection

A. the Cesterne.

B. the little washer.

C. the wast pipe.

D. the seate boord.

E. the pipe that comes from the Cesterne.

F. the Screw.

G. the Scallop shell to couer it when it is shut downe.

H. the stoole pot.

I. the stopple.

K. the current.

L. the sluce.

M.N. the vault into which it falles: always remember that ( ) at noone and at night, emptie it, and leaue it halfe a foote deepe in fayre water. And this being well done, and orderly kept, your worst priuie may be as sweet as your best chamber. But to conclude all this in a few wordes, it is but a standing close stoole easilie emptyed.

And by the like reason (other formes and proportions obserued) all other places of your house may be kept sweet.

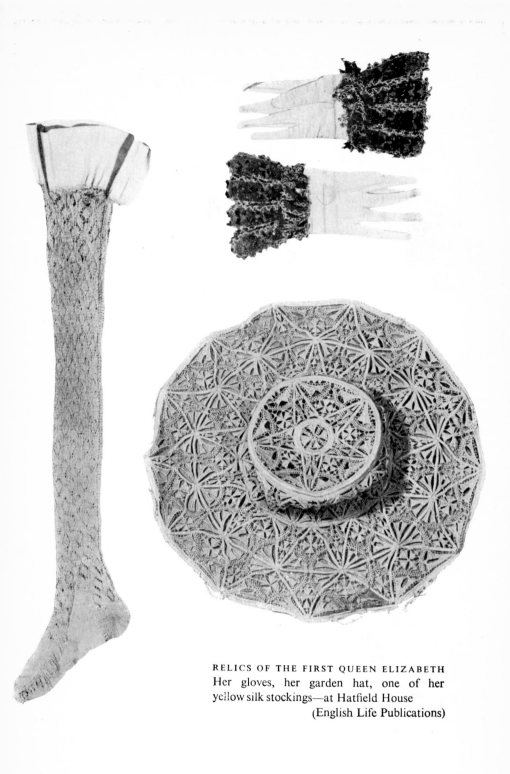

RELICS OF THE FIRST QUEEN ELIZABETH
Her gloves, her garden hat, one of her
yellow silk stockings—at Hatfield House
(English Life Publications)

NON SINE SOLE
IRIS.

THE RAINBOW PORTRAIT

The painting of the first Queen Elizabeth by Federigo Zuccaro (1543–1609), at
Hatfield House, reproduced by permission of the Marquess of Salisbury. In this
superb romantic portrait the Virgin Queen is represented as the fountain of wisdom,
her dress being decorated with eyes and ears enabling her to see all and hear all.

Whether or not we made an offer for the house is immaterial to this Introduction.   What *is* relevant is that, feeling ourselves to be reincarnated Elizabethans, we drove later in that afternoon through the great gates of Hatfield House in the neighbouring county of Hertfordshire. This had always been our favourite dream house of all, though we had been compelled to inspect it as mere sightseers, with no agent's Order to View. We felt we *must* end our Elizabethan day by looking again on some of the glories which Gloriana herself had known.

Once again—for we had often seen it before—we studied that romantic 'Rainbow' portrait.   Then we walked through the Great Hall to a case which held Gloriana's yellow silk stockings, her gloves, and her garden hat. At that moment we achieved something very near to success in J. W. Dunne's experiment with time. We were, for an immeasurable space of eternity, outside time. And, as we turned away, and slowly dropped back into the first year of the reign of Her Majesty Queen Elizabeth the Second, we experienced another tremor of historical excitement. For we realized that the house in which we stood belonged to one of Her Majesty's chief ministers of state, the Marquess of Salisbury, who is directly descended from William Cecil, Lord Burghley, the chief minister of Queen Elizabeth the First.

As we returned home and sat down to write our Introduction it seemed to us that personal coincidences and curiosities such as this meant much more to us than the Broad Aspects of History. The Elizabethans take on a personal reality for us when we examine their silk stockings and gloves and garden hats, or when we look up, as we did, at the tower of the Old Palace at Hatfield House and realize that from the window above us Elizabeth's unhappy sister Mary waved vainly to her father, as he rode past with averted face after divorcing her mother. Or, when we see in the park the very oak tree beneath which Elizabeth sat reading when the news of her accession was brought to her.

As we wrestled with our Introduction it occurred to us that as this is the first *Saturday Book* to appear in the new Elizabethan Age we ought to have some stirring signal to flash to our readers. It would be pleasant to do so, especially since the first Elizabeth was a sovereign in whom our increasing body of readers in the United States have an equal share. But somehow the stirring signal became confused with Drake's game of bowls. We kept on thinking about that attic in which Shakespeare discovered—no, not Titania, but Puck, perhaps, and certainly Bottom. And Elizabeth's garden hat and silk stockings. And poor Mary in the tower.

Perhaps, after all, those are the things which most concern our readers when they take up their *Saturday Book* and set aside more influential and responsible organs of opinion. We cast our thoughts back to inspiring events such as the repulse of the Armada. But before long our maritime investigations lead us to the pleasures of the pier. When we try to survey the History of Our Own Times we find it written in the Charleston and the cloche hat. We prefer insects and embroidery to Movements and Trends. We would rather gaze through Arthur Devis's vistas to the distant gazebo than consider the economic effects of the Seven Years' War. Even when we try to focus our attention on such awe-inspiring portents as guided missiles and the A, H, or is it now the Z? bomb, we find ourselves cutting out a woodcut of an Elizabethan whizzbang and sticking it at the bottom of the page.

Alas, we have no Serious Purpose to commend us. Indeed the only serious task which we have tackled—and, we observe, completed—is to fill the pages allotted for this Introduction to the twelfth, the largest, and, as our revered Founder has graciously assured us, not the least interesting issue of *The Saturday Book*.

J. H.

*To introduce the Repository of Marine Marvels which
follows we invited the Compleat Islander of our time to
set down some thoughts on islands he has collected*

The Island Life

by SIR COMPTON MACKENZIE

MOST nesophiles over sixty would probably attribute the very beginnings of their love of islands to three books read in childhood—*Robinson Crusoe, Coral Island,* and *The Swiss Family Robinson.* It is rash to generalize, but according to my enquiries these three books no longer stimulate the youthful imagination. Nevertheless, the idea of small islands is perhaps dearer to the hearts of our perplexed and harassed present than it ever was to an earlier age. Every year that passes makes man less and less able to call his body or even his mind his own, and he instinctively pines for the restricted space of a small island and the protection of the circumfluent sea because he feels that there he might regain the personal dignity of which the present time seeks ever more steadily and ever more relentlessly to deprive him. Contemporary humbug bleats about the 'free world.' Our bonds may be looser than those which strap the millions who have surrendered to Moscow's straitjacket for human existence, but to talk about the 'free world' is as meaningless a piece of self-flattery as 'Pretty Polly' in the mouth of a parrot.

Whether one could avoid the plague of bureaucratic forms by living in one of the small Channel Isles today I do not know, but I did succeed in escaping from them during the eight years in the 1920s when I lived on the island of Jethou, and I attribute whatever liveliness of mind I still possess to that blessed escape for awhile from the tyranny of the slave-state. Jethou could be called within my experience (and my experience is more extensive than that of most people in this regard) the most perfect small island within easy reach of a British port. The total area was fifty acres, which meant a mile's walk round it by the lower cliff path. That may sound a very short promenade, but when the compass is boxed in the course of a mile the variety of aspect and vegetation, the continuous expectation of a new bird or butterfly, and the intimate communion with the island's regular life combine to make such a mile worth ten on the mainland.

Even the Germans when they occupied Jethou in 1940 left it at peace. They did not cut down a single tree in the ancient grove of sweet chestnuts, pear trees and gnarled hawthorns : they did not lop a bough from the great mulberry over two centuries old that shaded half the grey-walled garden. They left the privateer's cannon where it had stood upon the cliff since the Napoleonic wars. They made less alterations to the garden than tenants who came after me and dug up the flowering plums and cherries I had planted to replace them with geraniums and lobelias. In fact they must have succumbed to the influence of the *genius loci*. Yes, there I lived for eight years without taxes or rates, without any contact, indeed, with bureaucracy except the very rare visit of a Treasury official, the Treasury administering the island for H.M. the King, who had inherited it from the Dukes of Normandy. Do not let it be supposed that I saved money by not paying rates and taxes : on the contrary I spent every farthing I could gather in from the books I wrote to serve that much-loved island.

To spend one's own hard-earned money in what one considered was the right way to spend it on a property held in trust without reference to District Councils or County Committees or Whitehall mandarins is beyond the aspirations of the great majority of those Britons who once upon a time were determined never to be slaves. I am humbly grateful to fortune.

The island of Herm on which I lived before I went to Jethou was only three-hundred acres in extent, but I found it too large to manage as a side-show to my own profession. In order to find money to restore buildings and maintain them, to put in good heart farmland which had been allowed to degenerate during the First World War, to keep boats in trim, and to provide for the health and comfort of the thirty odd people dependent upon me, I had to produce books faster than I wanted to produce them ; in doing that I was tied to my chair and unable to devote all my attention to the island itself.

One of the conditions of my lease from the Crown was to allow the famous shell beach to be visited twice a week by tourists who paid sixpence for the privilege, fourpence of which went to myself and twopence to the Crown. The shell beach at Herm is a marine wonder : some freak of the tides has amassed here the most astonishing collection of minute shells that may exist in the world. Unfortunately, many visitors were not content to walk along the beach to the shell beach ; having paid sixpence to land on Herm they believed that the whole island was theirs from that moment. The result was that for a couple of days every week from April to October we could not achieve privacy even in the granite-walled garden of the great manor house gothicized

THE ISLAND OF HERM   The lower photograph shows the shell beach

by my predecessor Prince Blücher to the bad imitation of a Rhineland castle. My library and writing-room was in a cottage looking out on this garden, and I was continually being disturbed by the intrusion of strangers. Once I protested that they were trespassing upon my privacy, which provoked the indignant comment: 'I thought we lived in a free country.'

And the litter! It took three of my farm-hands a long morning's work to tidy up the island after one of those twice-weekly invasions.

There was a miniature shell beach on Herm called Belvoir lying in a cove between green cliffs and thickets of blackthorn, the land behind sloping gradually up along a narrow valley down which a rivulet flowed to the sea. The shell beach proper was quite half a mile long with some fifty acres of level grassland innumerably starred in their season with burnet roses; one might have supposed that the visitors would be content with such a playground. Not at all. The mere fact of putting up a notice on the cliff-path that the approach to Belvoir was strictly private was enough to make every party determined to look for shells there, to bathe there, and to picnic there. I encouraged a Great Dane I had to carry off the women's underclothing that strewed the beach while they were in the water, and that was some satisfaction. Nevertheless, I had to recognize at last that twice a week Belvoir was a trippers' lounge.

Some three centuries ago a party of more civilized visitors came over to sing madrigals in Belvoir cove—Herm was then a pleasaunce of the Governor of Guernsey—and one of them in looking for shells lost a gold signet-ring. A descendant of him who lost that signet-ring visited Belvoir just after the First World War and while looking for shells found her ancestor's signet-ring; I believe it is now in the Guernsey Museum.

I quote from a romance of mine called *Fairy Gold* to describe the shells of Belvoir:

'The beach, which had the texture and colour of finely ground macaroons, appeared at a superficial glance to be formed of dry sand; but a closer inspection of this bright crescent shared by green land and green sea revealed that it was composed entirely of shells. They were of every shape and hue and degree of perfection—minute caps of liberty wrought from alabaster lace; fairy horns of ivory rose—dyed where they had touched the lips of their tiny trumpeters; large scallops piebald and iron-grey; infinitesimal fans that flamed against the light with elfin sunsets, and white cups that held in their hollows the flush of elfin dawns; sea-mussels dipped in damson-juice and wine; limpets spotted like pards; diminutive conches carmine-tipped; winkles of orange and citron; winkles of primrose and amber; winkles of cream and fawn, of chestnut, cinnamon and rich mahogany; lavender winkles lilac-slashed and diced with pearl.'

It is nearly thirty years since I set foot on Herm, but if I were put ashore there on a starless night in midwinter I would wager to walk round the island without missing my way, and there would be plenty of narrow cliff paths to negotiate. The caves along the eastern cliffs facing Sark are of great beauty and it requires a good deal of agility to visit all of them at a low spring tide. I doubt if many people have achieved the feat. Here from *Fairy Gold* is a description of one of those caves :

'The whole of the centre of the cave was occupied by a large pool, the sides of which were encrusted with red and rosy nullipores, whose calcareous deposits had left even the bare rock whence they had died off smoothly coated with the appearance of a lustrous mauve and lilac-pink enamel. The water was so pellucid that evidently it was refreshed by every high tide, and in one corner of it there was a bunch of dove-grey sea-anemones, each as large as a cactus-dahlia. The sides and roof of the cave were even more fantastic than this pool, being of every shade of murrey and sorrel and verd-antique and bloomed over a large space with a down that had the richness of plum-coloured velvet, but dripping apparently from every crack with blood, so that the shelving rocks above the pool were spattered with it.'

Besides the marine caves there was the adit of an old silver mine to explore, which meant plunging through sticky mud for over a hundred yards of candlelit cramped darkness. There was another adit to an old lead mine where one had to squeeze through a small opening in the rock to find oneself in an eerie cavern that would have held a company of soldiers.

There were two abandoned granite quarries, natural rockeries bright with flowers, and the Londoner who walks up the steps of the Duke of York's column to Waterloo Place may see here and there the word *Herm* carved upon them, for those steps are built of Herm granite.

I wonder if the German garrison in the last war was as much frightened by the Herm ghosts as the British garrison was in the first war. The late Herbert Hughes, who collected and arranged folk-songs with such exquisite taste, told me that the men under his command on Herm would never patrol except in pairs. The only time I have ever experienced the authentic panic of the Greeks was when I was looking for moths and mushrooms one breathless autumn evening near the desecrated cromlechs by the common. Suddenly I became aware of elemental spirits all round me and I ran a mile to the safety of glimmering cottage windows. Yes, Herm was (and probably still is) a haunted island ; pirates gibbeted along the northern shore, Celtic princes buried in those great cromlechs : bygone generations of dreamers, malefactors, lovers, mariners, witches, monks, prehistoric men and women, they have all left something of themselves behind. Prospero's isle seems completely credible here.

No, I do not regret the money I earned by writing twelve hours a day to maintain Herm for three years even if nothing of that tenancy now remains except the pines I planted to challenge the onset of the fierce sea-wind.

Three centuries ago Dorothy Osborne wrote :

'Do you remember Arme (Herm) and the little house there ? Shall we go thither ? That's next to being out of the worlde, there we may live like Baucis and Philemon, grow old together in our little cottage and for charity to some shipwrakt stranger obtaine the blessing of dying both at the same time.
How idly I talk !'

Alexander Selkirk on his island is made by the poet to say :

'I am monarch of all I survey,
My right there is none to dispute.'

If that were the only sentiment inspired by life on a small island it would reflect a feeble enough manifestation of egotism, and it may be doubted if a *coup d'oeil* of monarchy presents a tempting prospect to the would-be dweller on a small island. Anyway, I hope not, for it would be a barren experience if it did. I look back to those years on Jethou and when I remember with gratitude the escape they provided from the many nuisances of contemporary existence I remember with a deeper warmth the opportunity to live in concord with the birds, butterflies, flowers and trees that shared the island with me and with the rich variety of marine creatures that thronged its shores.

The only inhabitants of Jethou with which I had to go to war were the rabbits. A governor in the days of Queen Elizabeth introduced rabbits to Herm and Jethou for his own sport, and they have been a plague ever since. There is nothing to be said in favour of rabbits outside a child's story book. They share with slugs a wicked passion for the best plants in a garden. Some people can eat them : I cannot even enjoy that pleasure. Let me warn anybody who thinks of acquiring a small island to be sure that it is rabbitless. I abhor killing anything, but the rabbits on Herm and Jethou roused a blood lust in me by their foul behaviour and I shot hundreds of them every year. However, rabbits apart, the rule of a good island is to live and let live. Even eagles have the sense to observe this rule. It is recorded by a sixteenth-century topographer that the two white-tailed eagles which inhabited the Shiant Islands in the Minch never attacked the Shiant lambs, but always flew over to Lewis to seize their dinner. The descendants of those white-tailed eagles still had their eyrie on the Shiant Islands at the beginning of this century, when one of them was shot by a marauding collector, regrettably a clergyman, and when I bought the island in 1924 the eyrie had long been empty. I dreamed of building a house upon the Shiants, but in the end I did no more than make an old shepherd's bothy a place in which to camp out in high summer.

The Shiant Islands are in Gaelic the islands of the spell, and when I say that they offer the finest marine landscape in all Britain I run no risk of disturbing them with too many sight-seers, for they are difficult to reach on account of the turbulent overfalls that guard the approach to their shores and the curious visitor might easily be stranded there for a week. He would find no rabbits, but he would find innumerable large rats which grow fat on the eggs of the myriads of sea-birds, on the nestlings, and in winter on the limpets. These rats first arrived from the wreck of a Norwegian ship and have multiplied abominably.

With this warning I quote from MacCullough's description of the Western Isles of Scotland:

'To the north Gariveilan (the most conspicuous of the group) presents a long extended line of columnar cliffs; reaching in a perpendicular curve to 1,000 yards or more and impending in one broad mass of shadow over the dark sea that washes its base. The height of this range varies from 300 to 400 feet; and it thus forms the most magnificent colonnade to be found among the Western Islands. In simplicity and grandeur of effect it exceeds Staffa as much as it does in magnitude; offering to the tourist an object as worthy of his pursuit as that celebrated island, but lying beyond the boundary of ordinary travel, it is still unknown.'

And except to the adventurous few it will remain unknown. If the s.s. *Politician* had struck upon the shores of the Shiant Islands we might still be able to drink whisky galore.

THE SHIANT ISLANDS
Aquatint by William Daniell, 1819

BESIDE THE SEASIDE

BY

OLIVE COOK and EDWIN SMITH

Beside the Seaside

IT is odd to think of a time when there were no annual holidays by the sea, no piers, grand hotels or boarding-houses, when no one bathed or built sand castles, and when season after season the tides cast up their treasures of shell and seaweed and stirred the mysterious life of the rock pool unnoticed by human eye. Yet until a general appreciation of nature began to develop during the eighteenth century the sea was regarded as no more than a dangerous means of earning a livelihood.

It was not, however, feeling for nature alone that gave rise to Brighton and Blackpool, Scarborough and Southsea. Those early trips to the coast were made reluctantly and for reasons of health. The waters of inland spas were suddenly found to be medically inferior to the sea. The champion of the ocean was a fashionable London physician, Dr Richard Russell. He recommended a concoction of crabs' eyes, burnt sponge, vipers' flesh, cuttle-fish bones, snails, tar and a tincture of woodlice to be swallowed with a pint of seawater. 'This,' he comments, 'will be found commonly sufficient, in grown Persons, to give 3 or 4 smart stools.' But to complete the cure a dip in the sea itself was necessary.

There was no joy in the dip. Winter was considered to be the most beneficial time for the ceremony, for the pores of the skin had to be closed ; and the bather could neither dodge nor postpone the horrid moment of immersion, for he was at the mercy of the dipper. That extraordinary and, happily, defunct official, usually fierce and female, like the renowned Martha Gunn of Brighton, stood fully clothed, up to her thighs in the sea, by the door of the bathing machine, from which the victim was thrust into her embrace and plunged into the waves.

But just as the clumsy, voluminous bathing costumes of the last century yielded to the brief garments of today, so the seaside slowly came to be synonymous with all the pleasures of relaxation and revelling. Rounded bays and stucco terraces rose in their hundreds about our shores, elegant ironwork piers were flung out into the sea itself, and beneath the domed roof of the concert hall at its very end, nigger minstrels chanted nightly to sunburnt audiences. Fishermen forgot the grim exigencies of their calling as, smoking and yarn spinnning, they rowed trippers a few safe yards along the coast. And on the beach children made sandpies and moated fortresses, rode upon donkeys and crowded to watch a performance of Punch and Judy.

Amid all this frollicking, the daily draught of brine was long considered an essential part of a visit to the sea. But a more sympathetic follower of Dr Russell pointed out qualities in the salt waters which must have made them more palatable. 'They enliven, invigorate and actuate the whole mass of the blood,' he said, 'to a sweet, balsamick, spiritous and sanguinous temperament, which naturally incites men and women to amorous emotions and titillations.'

The rapid development of seaside entertainment was accompanied by increasing awareness of the variety and fascination of the shore itself, that salt-blanched strip of shingle or sand, of chalk or granite, where even the flowers are pale, papery and remote.

The pleasure of this strange world are those of form, colour and texture. Soft sand is patterned with delicate curves and ridges by the receding wave, and mirrors the sky, the white breasts of gulls and the darting motion of the sandpiper. Every tide exposes some new, enchanting shell shape : pink, yellow and orange fans ; large, striated Venus shells ; razors, lime green, purple and brown, shining as though freshly varnished; white and violet tops tipped with pink ; augurs like unicorn horns ; mottled limpets ; and whelks stained green and rose and prettily clustered about by acorn barnacles. The pebble beach looks the colour of a dove's wing against the sea, but if you walk where the breakers fall the stones shine with the brilliance of jewels, dark red, smoky blue, grass green, velvety black, amber and pearl white. Some are spotted like eggs or striped like candies, some are lightly encircled with hairfine lines of slate grey, others are boldly patterned in white so that they resemble Oceanic masks. In the rock pool the Father Lasher starts from a thicket of weeds like gigantic dock leaves, and sets in movement delicate fronds of white and palest lilac and long brown streamers, as beaded and scaly as dragon claws. Red and pink anemones open with the tide and appear like dahlias blossoming under the sea. From the rocks above the pool hang bunches of tiny, transparent glassy balls, or singly they lie on the beach, sparkling more brightly than diamonds.

All these and many more marvels, as well as the gaiety of the concert party and the brass bedstead and rose-decked wash-basin of the old-fashioned lodging house, make up the special world into which we step when the train draws up at the seaside platform. They are implicit already in the salty tendrils of the convolvulus which twine about the station railings, and assure us that we are indeed beside the seaside.

Scene at Sandbath by John Leech (1817–1864) 'The female Blondin outdone! Grand morning
performance on the narrow plank by the darling. . . .'
Lithographic print coloured by the artist (Louis Meier)

East Parade, Bognor. Edwardian postcard
(Charles Bretherton)

MARY ANNING of Lyme Regis (Nat. Hist. Mus.)

On left, top to bottom: A STURGEON, aquatint by William Daniell, 1809.

PEGWELL BAY, 1858, by William Dyce, R.A. (Tate Gal.). The figures are the artist's wife, in striped shawl, her sisters and Dyce's son.

OYSTERS, aquatint by William Daniell, 1809.

THE LARGE-EYED POMATOME, engraving by Lizars, early 19th cent.

Below: FOSSIL FISH from the Lower Lias, Lyme Regis (Nat. Hist. Mus.)

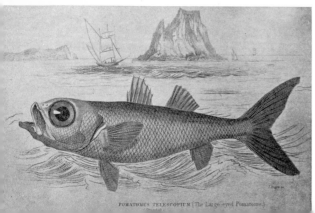

POMATOMUS TELESCOPIUM (The Large-eyed Pomatome.)

In 1811 Mary Anning, then only a child, discovered the gigantic fossil of the Ichthyosaurus Platydon in the lias mud at Lyme Regis. Since then few visitors to Lyme return without some example of fossil fish or ammonite. On other shores the patterns left by tides, varieties of seaweeds, those 'flowers of the sea,' shells, pebbles, anemones, sea urchins and starfish entice us to play the naturalist and sometimes to comb the beach, like the mussel gatherers in *Pegwell Bay*, with a more practical end in view.

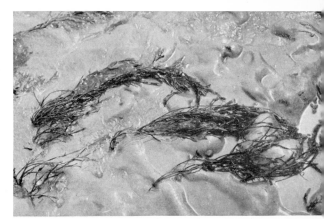

While Victorian children, undismayed by boots and long drawers, were enjoying the newly discovered pleasures of castle building and shrimping, Philip Gosse, stern parent and opponent of Darwin, was wandering by the rock pools of Devon and Pembrokeshire, recording for the first time in exquisitely drawn and coloured lithographs, the flowery forms of anemones and starfish, the mottled, metallic gleam of the ancient wrasse and the shapes of plush and silken weeds, stranger than any earthly foliage, forked and fanned, flat and thread-like, frilly or straight and streaming, purple, green, pink, white and brown. The brilliance of this silent, swaying paradise far outdoes the gaiety of the children's dresses, and straw hat and billowing skirt appear homely indeed beside the swelling dome of the parasite anemone.

Opposite: The Parasite Anemone (*The Aquarium*, 1854)
The Common Shrimp (*A Year at the Shore*, 1865)
The Ancient Wrasse (*The Aquarium*, 1854)
Lithographs by Philip Gosse (Nat. Hist. Mus.)
Above: 'Sand Castles' Victorian Lithograph (Louis Meier)
Below: 'On the Sea Shore' Lithograph by A. F. Lydon, from *Sea-Side Walks*, 1870

From the West Pier, Brighton

The Sands Margate, 1868

Cliff-top Terrace, Tenby

Our older seaside resorts were Regency creations, and clean, spray-drenched, stucco facades are as much a part of Brighton, Margate, Ramsgate and Hastings as the plaint of gull and oystercatcher. It is fitting that the Prince Regent's most striking memorial, the fantastic Pavilion, should have become almost a symbol of Brighton. Bathing machines, now alas almost extinct, originated in the same period and were inseparable from that formidable institution, the dipper. Even the modern grand hotel, its myriad panes flashing back the morning sun, retains something of Regency flavour, while here and there in some humbler hostel, a bed-chamber recalls the kind that must have been let with "two parlours, pantry, etc., for 5s. a week" in about 1810.

Grand Hotel, Brighton

Victorian souvenir cup

THE TURNSTONE

Wood engraving by Thomas Bewick, 1809

Herring Gull

Bedroom, Seaside Hotel

The Cockle Sheds, Leigh-on-Sea

Victorian souvenir paper-weight

Bathing machines, Llandudno

Porcelain plate. Worcester, 1807–13
(V. and A. Mus.)

Earthenwa

Right: Herring Girl. Staffordshire
(Margaret Boxwell)

Below: Pot lid (George Ward)

Adair)

Porcelain plate. Worcester? (Mary Adair)

In the first gay years of our perplexed century the sea-side resort and the picture postcard reached their apex of popularity. The life portrayed in these Edwardian cards, them-selves a peculiarly moving combination of photo-graphy and hand litho-graphy, is enchanting, striped, spacious, magi-cally motorless.

Victorian scrap

Staffordshire pottery (E. Dere)

From 'Sketches at Trouville in 1879' by
Randolph Caldecott (Louis Meier)

Edwardian postcard

'Do Mamma let me have a dip.'
Engraving by C. Dawe

Though Sir Edward Poynter's mermaid and the siren made from seafoam wear no costume, the emancipation of Victorian ladies from the 'flannel cases' which 'showed nothing but their handsome faces' was in reality but recent. Spoon's *Household Manual* of 1890 still describes dresses for swimmers, for non-swimmers and for ladies bathing with gentlemen, all characterized by ample folds.

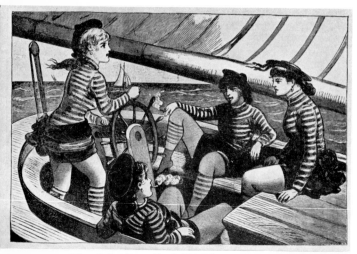

'We sail the Ocean Blue,' *The Police Gazette*, 1890's

Shell Mermaid (Brighton Museum)

Mermaid Flask, brown earthenware, early 19th cent.
(Mrs Leonard Russell)

Carved Meerschaum pipe (Astley's, Jermyn Street)

Figurehead at Southwold, 19th century

'At Low Tide,' by Sir Edward Poynter, P.R.A.
(Pears Annual, 1914)

Of the three seashore surfaces, sand and shells are more easily pleasing to the eye in search of decoration or the foot seeking comfort. Yet, by contrast with its apparent barrenness, the treasures of a pebbly beach can be unbelievably beautiful, as we bend above the moist fringe of the tide or dip the sun-dried stone into a pool to varnish its colour. Even a fragment of brick or tile or bright blue bottle glass, worn smooth and round by the tumbling waves is worth its place in our returning luggage.

A Sand bell by W. Carpenter (Mrs Leonard Russell) and a Sand Picture by Zobell (Henry Swanzy), both of Shanklin Chine, and made in the natural coloured sands of the cliffs of Alum Bay, Isle of Wight

Shell Picture of an Italian church by Miss Jane Parminter (Miss M. L. R. Tudor)

Punch and Judy show on the sands at Weymouth

Chalked 'Cruse Notice,' Southend

The seaside resort is the spiritual home of popular art. Indeed, almost all the perquisites of the promenade, bandstands and bathing machines, pink rock, pebble sweets and postcards, piers and paddleboats, lighthouses and lobster pots have that air of salty simplicity, that mixture of artlessness and artfulness, which we call the 'folk.'

Paddlebox of South Coast pleasure steamer

Sand Picture 'Shankline Chine,' mid-19th century (Mrs Mark Lubbock).

Chair made of gull's feathers (Brighton Mus.)

Postcard Stall, Brighton

Pictures on the sand, from Southend pier

A nicer example of the obscure fitness of things could nowhere be found than that two principals of seaside pleasures should share, without relationship, the name of Gosse: Philip, guide to the pool, where urchin, shrimp and shellfish reveal nature in her folk art phase; and William, originator of 'Crest' china, summit of marine popular art.

Net Store and model boats by Mr James Ovett, Brighton

The Lighthouse
Isle of Portland

Gosse 'Crest' china, early 20th cent. (Mr Tom Ingram)

Lithographed Song Cover, late 19th century
(Barry Duncan)

Seaside Slot Machine, by Mr Leonard Lee
(British Automatic Company)

Brighton Pierrots, by W. R. Sickert (Morton H. Sands)

Heading of Concert Advertisement, 1837

Carrick's Original Pierrots, Scarborough, *c.* 1900

The pleasures of the seaside are not confined to weeds and winkles; there is more to it than promenading and paddling. Though it may now cost three pennies to go on the pier, one penny will still produce the jerky terrors of the execution or the excitement of a fire, will predict your future or reveal the uncertainties of conjugal life. Though the seashell polka, together with black stockings and boaters, is a memory of the past, we are still entertained by carnival and pierrot as we sit nipped behind the knees by our deck chairs, sand between our toes, our critical faculties delightfully softened by the salt air and the pulse of the sea

Riley's Revellers, Herne Bay, *c.* 1912

The Olympian Concert Party, Eastbourne, 1915. Harry Kemp, Winnie Tee, Jack Rickards and Ernest Pitt

Southsea Carnival, 1923

Seaweed picture.
The Avenue, by
Miss Jane Parminter
(1750–1811) (Miss
M. Tudor)

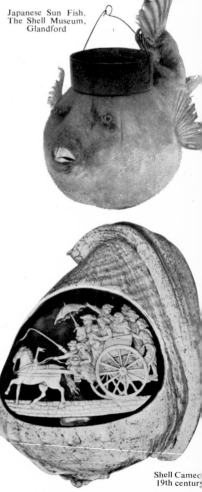

Japanese Sun Fish,
The Shell Museum,
Glandford

Shell Cameo
19th century

Shell and feather mosaics at À la Ronde, near Exmouth, Devon

Call us not weeds we are flowers of the sea,
For lovely, and bright and gay tinted are we,
And quite independent of sunshine or shower,
Then call us not weeds, we are Oceans gay flowers.

Not fanned by the winds of a summers parterre,
Whose gales are but sighs of an evening air,
Our beliefs, fragile, and exquisite forms,
Are nurs'd by the billows, and rock'd by the storm.

Shaped and smoothed by the rhythm of the waves, the products of the sea are more aesthetically perfect than any natural objects and satisfy more readily than any others the creative propensities of the amateur. A dried and hollow fish with an incredibly human expression becomes a lantern; a frame of pelican-foot shells and a foreground of seaweeds give a rich, salty flavour to a marine print; dried seaweeds of every shade of brown and pink make a basket of fragile flowers or clothe the trees of an autumnal landscape. But the most ambitious use of shells and seaweeds is surely the decoration of the octagon at À la Ronde. The Misses Jane and Mary Parminter had travelled in Italy and aspired to recreate in their Regency House some of the features of San Vitale, Ravenna. The walls of the central hall are encrusted, like the Byzantine church, with mosaics, executed not in glass and stone, but in shells, seaweeds and feathers, all gathered with remarkable industry from the Devonshire coast. It is one of the most charming follies in a period of delightful fantasy

Shell Roundel (*George Groves*)

Beach photographers' properties
Brighton

Siesta,
Eastbourne, 1927

A warning notice, South Devon

The Rescue, *Every Boy's Annual*, 1868

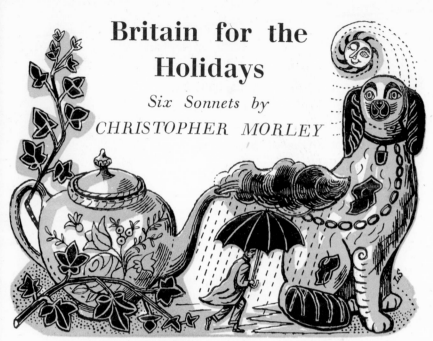

Britain for the Holidays

Six Sonnets by
CHRISTOPHER MORLEY

With Decorations by Laurence Scarfe

I

The emblems of a British holiday
Outwitting the austerities of Cato
Are the raincoat not too far away,
Potato and potato and potato.
The tiny car, rebuilt, is 'running in';
Chop cabbage and smoke haddock and steam kipper,
Invoke the sausage with the vellum skin
That ought to be provided with a zipper.

Great Britain queues up for an hour of sun;
Never basked so many in hours so few,
Nowhere so many parked wrongside; drive slow!
Bless pleasure-hungry Britons, every one,
And grant them, so good-humoredly in queue,
Their acme of approval: *Not a bad show.*

45

II

The Island Race, set forth on leg and wheel,
Likes what it knows, and knows just what it likes:
Plenty of mustard on its ham-and-veal;
Not open roads, but those well filled with bikes.
Pack in enduring infants, ditto dogs.
At temperatures of seventy-plus they sizzle,
And if belike there happen rains and fogs
These are accepted as refreshing drizzle.

Prepare the buns-and-butter, the fish fritter!
And, as goal and goblet of adventures,
The brimming mugs of tepid mild-and-bitter
To rinse the busy governmental dentures.
Wrapped in oilskins, under dripping trees,
A stalwart people seek 'amenities.'

46

III

Admit, Britannia has 'bright intervals'—
One slice of sun, as thin as buttered crust,
Mosses are emerald mice on roofs and walls,
She sheds her muffles, yearns to be untrussed.
But aspen lifts white petticoats to the gust:
The glass percussed, it steadies? No, it falls.
Britannia robes again, proving as she must
Connoisseur of climate; scholar of squalls.

Here in a royal seigniory of oak
Watching clouds that sag uncertainly
I smell the southwest in sweet cottage-smoke
And think it prudent to stay in for tea.
Britain, sun-and-rainshot till she spangles
Has been tough education for the Angles,

47

IV

I saw three swans in Friday sunset flying;
Evening's golden lances pierced the wood;
Lawn and cricket field were slowly drying;
Meseemed the meteorology was good.
There was a rainbow showing the full prism,
Weatherwise Girl Guides were pitching camp;
My ankles were not grieved with rheumatism,
Even bedroom sheets were hardly damp.

I dined, and answered with a keen digestion
The familiar treble-British question
Thick or clear? sweet, savoury? black or white?
Orion glittered cap-à-pie that night.
Everything was Ticking Over. — Then
The morn, and the morn's morn, it rained again.

V

And now we settle for the autumn drowse :
The bee, snapdragon-trapped, turns in and snores ;
Dogs idle in mid-scratch ; men gape like cows.
Ripeness is all. Lethargy is outdoors.
By harvest-shaven fields the old blue bus
At cottages and farm-lanes tremble–stopping,
Missus heaves aboard, mornings all of us
Who trundle in to Lymington for shopping.

Tiles are newly gilt with pats of lichen,
Window-plants and dahlias are ablaze,
Plum-and-wasp is boiling in the kitchen,
Oilywoite is Tennysonian haze—
And I remember, bumping on the road,
It was in Hampshire that Keats wrote the Ode.

49

VI

Poets are always foreigners; they see clear
In the lens of other poets' eyes:
What half-familiar flowers to recognize,
What durable trees; birds with accents, hear!
Visit and search, enchantment multiplies:
The mortal miracle is very near
When alien weather under alien skies
Is equally rare, and commonplace, and dear.

The English oak is packed with acorns still
While Paumanok seres in yellow, pink, and rust.
Whence and wherever love's contagion grew,
We dream of kindred anguish to fulfill:
Keats sickened here; Hardy breathed cider-must;
There are the leaves of grass Walt Whitman knew.

CHRISTOPHER MORLEY

Hampshire, August–September 1951.

50

An Artist on the Seine

Pages from the sketch-book of

ROBERT GIBBINGS

THE wood-engravings of Robert Gibbings, which have become
familiar to many thousands of readers in his books on the
Thames, the Wye, Ireland and the South Seas, are remarkable
for their precision and clean cutting. It is probably not realized that
Mr Gibbings makes many drawings before committing his designs to
the wood. By chance we happened to see in his studio a number of
these preliminary sketches, made as working 'notes' for his coming
book on the Seine. After much persuasion he allowed us to reproduce
some of them in the following pages.

THE upper reaches of the Seine, which Robert Gibbings has been
exploring for his next book, are even more secluded than the
upper reaches of the Thames. There are no footpaths. The
river is hedged by poplar plantations.

Moret-sur-loing. The Loing is one of the loveliest tributaries of the Seine, and the most 'fishy.' Trout, chub, roach, pike, barbel, carp, perch, all are there in quantities, and fishermen are there in shoals.

CROSSING the Boulevard Montparnasse, the Boulevard Raspail, sketched below, marks the centre of the artists' quarter on the left bank of the Seine.

THE River Douix (opposite) issues wide and clear from under a massive chalk cliff. It is only a hundred and fifty paces in length before it joins the Seine, but even then it is as wide as the Seine, which has already run some thirty miles.

THE Pont Sully, under which, as under
the Pont Mirabeau in the words of
Apolinaire, 'coule la Seine et nos amours.'

LOOKING from rue Saint Julien
le Pauvre to rue Galande, two
of the oldest streets in Paris.

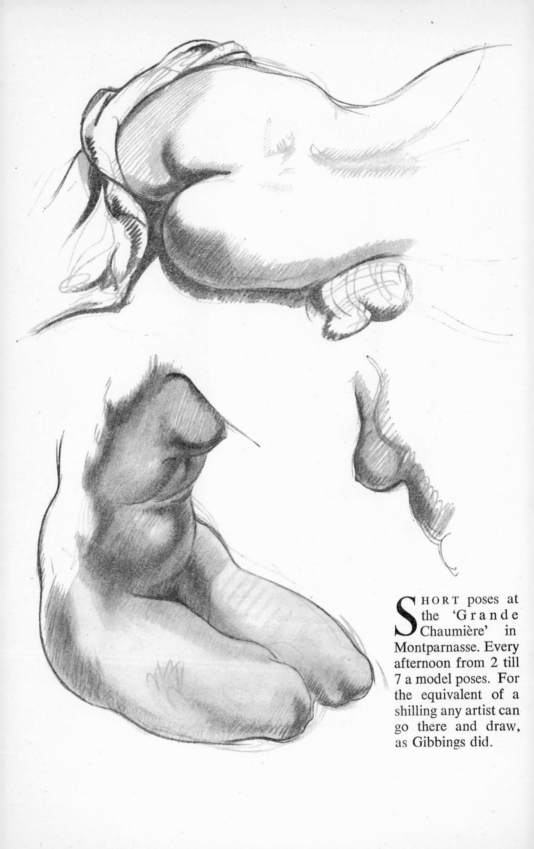

HORT poses at the 'G r a n d e Chaumière' in Montparnasse. Every afternoon from 2 till 7 a model poses. For the equivalent of a shilling any artist can go there and draw, as Gibbings did.

*As Robert Gibbings's pencil sketches the beauty of nakedness,
so Edwin Smith's camera records the beauty of adornment—
of embroideries treasured in the finest collection in Britain*

Embroidered in White

by OLIVE COOK

No one who entered the room casually would guess at the
magnificent treasures of lace and embroidery folded away in
the drawers of the long, broad table and in the ceiling-high
cupboards. One or two needlework pictures, a sampler and an
embroidered handkerchief, framed to show both sides of the work,
merely hint at their owner's interests and scarcely attract the eye from
the wide window overlooking tennis courts and a block of flats. But
as the heavy drawers slide open the view from the window fades. The
white-clad figures at the nets give way to the white garments of other
ages as Mr Jacoby lifts them from their silk and tissue-paper wrappings.

Soon a pile of exquisitely light fabrics lies on the table: muslins,
said to have been blanched with lemon water and called by poetic
Indian names which have long since fallen into disuse, dew of light,
running water, woven wind, scorched tears; and other kindred materials
such as barège, grenadine, jaconet and tarlatan. Transparent capes
and fichues charge this modern apartment with all the atmosphere of
the Bath Assembly Rooms. Here is a cap that might have been worn
by Mrs Allen or Mrs Thorpe; there is a coquettish little apron which
instantly recalls the familiar story of how Beau Nash, at odds for once
with fashion, tore such an adornment from the person of the Duchess
of Queensbury and flung it into a corner. A French muslin shawl,
perfectly plain except for an enchanting, narrow border, eloquently
proclaims neo-classic simplicity.

It is, however, not so much the shape and material of these articles
as the decoration upon them which so sharply distinguishes them from
the products of our own time. All are embroidered by hand, the
creation of tranquil, unhurried hours such as our age, with all its so-
called leisure, can never enjoy.

A large apron of diaphanous muslin (pl. 1) embroidered in very fine
linen thread in close outline stitch and pulled work combines the
characteristics of Queen Anne ornament with delightful individual
invention and humour in the treatment of detail. It is as though a
high wind, presumably from the East, had blown through the stiff, con-

59

ventionalized patterns of the previous century, scattering the motives loosely but rhythmically over the material, bending and curling stem, leaf and petal until the peacocks, whose crests and tails break into richly varied plant forms, the fantastic flowers and the insects with feelers like Ionic volutes make a design which perfectly harmonizes with the Chinese wallpapers and Indian chintzes of the period.   The eighteenth-century passion for the Orient also decides the character of a cover from Saxony (pl. 3a).   It is responsible not only for the intro-duction of a palm tree in the central medallion, but also for the Chinese aspect of the principal tree and for the willowy, linear feeling of the whole conception.   In the medallion itself the needle has aped the pencil to show with an astonishing variety of stitches a charioted princess appearing with Cupid in the clouds to a warrior accompanied by Minerva.   It is a scene which belongs essentially to German court life of the mid-eighteenth century.   Perhaps it commemorates one of the innumerable spectacular performances of French operettas at the court of Saxony, when the stage was set in the open air with a natural landscape and a lake behind it; or perhaps it refers to one of the annual occasions described by Justinius Kerner in his memoirs when, at a fête held on a lake, the pretty daughter of a notable citizen appeared as queen of the sea and was greeted with an ode in French alexandrines.

Anyone looking through this collection of white embroidery must be struck by the fact that the majority of the examples belong to the eighteenth and nineteenth centuries.   The art must have been prac-tised in other ages, but apart from the profusely ornamented table and altar linen of Renaissance Italy there seems little evidence of its popularity in former periods.   Yet so greatly was white upon white favoured at the beginning of the last century that, in at least one instance in this collection, it has been preferred to colour for a piece of needlework undertaken for pure pleasure, an amusing Swiss panel (pl. 3b) embroidered with figures and lettering, an elegant A and B which might have served as models for one of Imre Reiner's foliage sprouting types.   Even peasant embroidery, usually brilliantly coloured, was affected by this enthusiasm for white.   Nineteenth-century French cap crowns are enriched with floral motives which vary according to the village of origin.   This peasant work (pl. 2a) is distinguished from more sophisticated embroidery not only by a less developed sense of form, but by a spiky, feverish intensity of detail such as we find in some primitive paintings or automatic drawings.

How is this predilection for white to be explained?   It is perhaps natural that white should have been chosen for piqué and quilted work

Opposite: Part of a Queen
Anne muslin apron

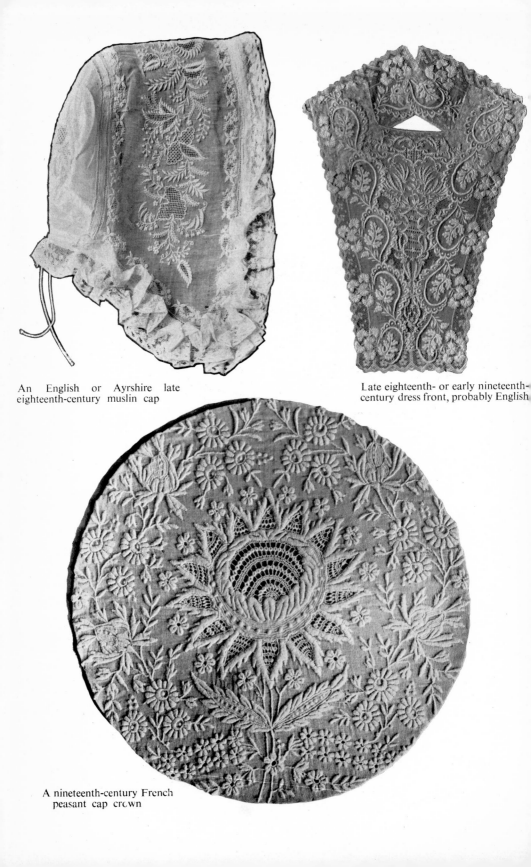

An English or Ayrshire late
eighteenth-century muslin cap

Late eighteenth- or early nineteenth-
century dress front, probably English

A nineteenth-century French
peasant cap crown

Princesse de vos Trails que vos
douces charmes
Minerve meme seule etemble par
ses armes

3a. *Above:* The central medallion of
an embroidered muslin cover, made
in Saxony

3b. *Below:* Swiss nineteenth-century
embroidery

where the basis of the ornament was white linen, and fine examples of this type of embroidery, in the form of bedspreads, waistcoats and caps, are a distinctive part of the output of the eighteenth century. It is understandable also that great impetus must have been given to white work by the introduction into Europe of Indian muslin at the beginning of Queen Anne's reign and by the later manufacture of the material, first in England and then in other European countries. But there were, in addition, psychological reasons for the popularity of white. During the age of Pamela, Clarissa and Werther, and again during the Victorian era, white was prized for its symbolic significance. White was above all symptomatic of the gradual waxing of enthusiasm during the eighteenth century for Greek and Roman antiquity. Neo-classic ladies tried to resemble ancient statues, and as these were presumed always to have been of marble pallor, the scanty, filmy garments of the eighteen-tens had to be white.

Very little is known of the embroiderers themselves. Though much of the work must have been the creation of the wearers of the garments, many pieces of embroidery were probably carried out to order by establishments whose products were associated with particular districts. The pleasing, open-work embroidery called *broderie anglaise,* though it is not English at all, is associated with Ayrshire. Agents from Scottish firms were also active in the establishment of embroidery centres in Ireland during the last century, and a school at Belfast is mentioned as having existed since 1700. We know that when the taste for Chinoiserie was at its height garments were cut to the required shape and dispatched to China or to the East Indies to be embroidered. It is characteristic of Chinese work that the design appears the same on both sides of the material. Two workers sat on either side of a frame and pushed the needle through from one side to the other.

Haunting likenesses between different pieces of embroidery sometimes suggest a common source, but their origin is usually no more than a matter for conjecture. It is part of the charm of this essentially feminine art (for we hear little of male embroiderers in Europe after the decline of the guilds) that it leaves so much to the play of imagination and resists classification. Catalogued no more precisely than as capes, caps, collars, handkerchiefs, shawls, aprons, babies' dresses, waistcoats and miscellaneous, these tangible and moving memories of the past are once more put away. The drawers are closed, the room resumes the smooth impersonality of shut doors and polished surfaces. Outside, the hollow impact of tennis ball and racquet resounds against the towering façade of the flats.

Opposite: Nineteenth-century French embroidery. The backing consists entirely of drawn work, giving the impression of lace

Palmerston, Lady Holland, Macaulay, Bulwer Lytton—
this was the kind of 'week-end' company to be found at The
Grove, amid Old Masters, galaxies of flowers, scores of
servants, meals of incredible richness—and one bathroom

Glories of The Grove

by GERALD HYDE VILLIERS

T HERE must still be quite a number of people alive who can
remember the days when Society did not consider it *de rigueur*
to depart from London on Saturday. For one thing, first nights
were always fixed for Saturday, so as to leave time on Sunday
for more rehearsals and possible changes. The first night of a
Gilbert and Sullivan or a Pinero play, for instance, was a social event
of the first magnitude. Then there was Church Parade on Sunday
morning. From the Achilles statue to Albert Gate, Hyde Park was
thronged with *le beau monde,* the ladies in their best bibs and tuckers,
the gentlemen in top hats, fawn-coloured waistcoats, patent leather
boots, and grey suede gloves. Nowadays you would have to look long
and far to find male hands encased in suede gloves. Then, to appear
without them at Church Parade was to court social ostracism. Sunday
luncheons were another regular institution, and 'cruising for cutlets'
was a recognized pursuit among the little brothers of the rich.

In those pre-motoring days week-end parties in the country were not the universal custom which they have since become, but they were not in any way exceptional. Round about four o'clock on a Saturday afternoon in summer you would have found outside most railway stations in the home counties a waiting carriage and pair, and on the box a coachman 'rosy-gilled, with fat close-clipped grey whiskers and inscrutably pursed lips, presiding high up in the easterly air like an emblem of the feudal system,' to quote Mr Galsworthy.

At a still earlier date, beyond the memory of anyone now alive, the week-end parties of my grandparents, the 4th Earl and Countess of Clarendon, at The Grove, near Watford, Herts, were deservedly famous, and invitations thereto were highly prized. Lord Clarendon, who was Secretary of State for Foreign Affairs no less than three times, and who could have been Prime Minister had he so desired, was in the innermost councils of the Whig leaders, who forgathered at The Grove and discussed the iniquities of Mr Disraeli and how best to effect that villain's discomfiture. When the present Lord Clarendon sold The Grove, *The Times* of February 20, 1936, came out with a leader deploring the passing of

one of the great political houses of the nineteenth century. In these degenerate days it may be necessary to call it The Grove, Watford (as though it were first cousin to 'The Laurels' or 'The Acacias,') but to our grandfathers, Broadlands, Brocket, Woburn, or The Grove needed no suffixes. . . . Thanks to its nearness to London, The Grove must have been one of the first houses where the practice of Saturday to Monday visiting (as the week-end habit was then called) was in force. That great diarist Greville records staying there with the Palmerstons, Lady Holland, Macaulay, Luttrell and Bulwer Lytton. The amusements of such a company, which principally consisted in conversation, might make no great appeal to the modern mind. Yet there may be some who would gladly turn off the wireless, lock up the cocktails, and clear out the bridge tables, if only they might listen to Macaulay's talk and hear expressions of Lady Holland's wit.

My grandfather would not have achieved his great career unless he had been a man of outstanding ability; and it is no disparagement of his abilities to say that his career was helped by the irresistible charm and perfect manners to which all his contemporaries bear witness. The late Marquess Curzon of Kedleston used to tell the following tale as an instance of perfect manners, the best instance, indeed, that he had ever come across. The tale was repeated to me by Mr Harold Nicolson, but it is not included in his excellent biography of the noble Marquess.

On hot summer nights the Clarendons frequently drove down to The Grove from London after dinner and slept there, without giving previous notice to the servants. A bedroom on the ground-floor was kept in readiness for them. One dark night, just after they had gone to bed, the french window opened quietly and a stable-hand crept stealthily into the room. Approaching the bed, the lout saw that it contained two figures. 'On which of you two darlings shall I begin?' he asked, with a chuckle. 'I pray, Sir,' replied Lord Clarendon with perfect composure, 'that I, at any rate, may be spared your no doubt well meant, but most unwelcome, attentions.'

I am glad that I was born in time to see something of the glories of The Grove, where my parents and their offspring used to spend Christmas with my uncle, who succeeded my grandfather as 5th Earl of Clarendon in 1870. It was not only a luxurious house; it was extremely comfortable, which by no means follows as a matter of course. All the senses were gratified, including the visual sense, and the pleasures of the eye can be very great. There is nothing displeasing to the eye in bone-handled table knives, plain electro-plate forks and spoons, and buff-coloured 'utility' plates; but they do not give active pleasure like a Georgian silver dinner service, silver-handled crested knives, silver rat-tail forks and spoons, the exotic birds and gay posies of flowers on Worcester and Crown Derby dessert services. There were a good number of dessert services at The Grove, and we never had the same one twice running. My favourite, though by no means the most valuable, was dark blue and white, with a different Aesop's fable in the centre of each plate and each dish. The dinner-table was either a sea of flowers, arranged by the head gardener with consummate skill, or it was nearly hidden under pyramids of fruit—white hot-house grapes, incredibly glossy apples, Tangerine oranges, and the traditional Christmas almonds and raisins. But let us return, not to our saddles of mutton, since that most excellent food, equally delectable hot or cold, is no longer to be found in these islands, but to the house itself.

The front door opened into a square hall, where hung the immense Gobelins tapestry of the Miraculous Draught of Fishes, after the cartoon by Raphael, which the Emperor Napoleon III presented to my grandfather in 1856 after the signature of the Treaty of Paris at the end of the Crimean War. The Emperor at the same time gave my grandfather one of the two eagle's quills which were used for the signature of the Treaty, and it is now in my possession. On the left of the hall was the dining-room, the first of a truly noble suite of rooms. It was large and square, with a white and gold ceiling, white and gold side-tables and chairs, and a flock wall-paper of a lovely shade of darkish green. Here hung some of the best pictures, notably the big Vandyck of the 16th Lord and Lady Derby, i.e. Charlotte de la Trémoïlle, who defended Lathom House in Lancashire against the Roundheads in 1644, and their small daughter; a half-length of Lucius Cary, Lord Falkland, by Vandyck; a full-length of George Villiers, 1st Duke of Buckingham, by Cornelius Jansen, one of the few portraits of that shameless scoundrel which gives an idea of his good looks; and a particularly good Lely of Henry Hyde, afterwards 2nd Earl of Clarendon, and his wife, *née* Lady Theodosia Capel, who according to the de Grammont Memoirs had by long practice subdued her glances to such a languishing tenderness that her eyes never opened more than those of a Chinese. I never cared much for the big Vandyck of the Derbys, but it was generally considered the show-piece of the collection. Some years before his death, in 1914, my uncle sold it for £32,000. It went to the United States, but I do not know if it is there now.

Next to the dining-room was the drawing-room, which led through a wide opening—no doors—into the library. These two rooms were really passage rooms, and no one ever sat in them. The drawing-room walls were hung with crimson silk, which made a background of great splendour for the full-length portraits in Sunderland frames by Vandyck and other seventeenth-century artists. Among them were three superb full-length Vandycks of Queen Henrietta Maria ; William Herbert, 3rd Earl of Pembroke, in black silk, relieved by the brilliant blue of the Garter ribbon round his neck, and the Garter star on his mantle ; and William Villiers, 1st Viscount Grandison, wearing a vermilion jerkin embroidered with gold, lace collar and cuffs, buff-coloured high boots with blue bows, and a black hat with a blue feather. All these pictures once formed part of the famous collection of Edward Hyde, 1st Earl of Clarendon and Lord Chancellor of England, who was not even remotely related to the family of Villiers. He can never have surmised that one day his pictures of members of the Villiers family would be in the possession of an Earl of Clarendon bearing that famous name.

The drawing-room ceiling had an elaborate gold enrichment in the centre. A grand piano stood between the french windows, and there were some good pieces of Louis XVI furniture. The white and gold bookshelves in the library reached up to three-quarters of the height of the walls, and above them hung half-length family portraits by Kneller, Dahl, Wissing, etc., many of them charming, but hung too high to see properly. Above the very ornate white marble chimneypiece was an equally ornate white and gold carved overmantel, framing the well-known and often reproduced half-length of the Chancellor Clarendon in his official robes, by Sir Peter Lely.

Next came the inner library, a large, beautiful and cheerful room, in which we all forgathered. It must have formed two rooms at one time, and across the ceiling at the join was a highly polished mahogany beam with gold enrichments, matching the mahogany and gold book-shelves. Above the latter hung pictures similar to those in the library. The light yellow silk window curtains went wonderfully well with the polished mahogany. The inner library was always full of flowers, and at Christmas time the flowers were gardenias and stephanotis. My mother thought that there were too many, and that their scent was overpowering. Perhaps she was right, but at the time I thought quite differently. To this day the scent of gardenias and stephanotis fills me with acute nostalgia.

Adjoining the inner library was the brown and gold small dining-room. Over the mantelpiece hung a picture of our great ancestor, Oliver Cromwell. Incidentally, there is another regicide among Villiers ancestors in the person of Count Montgomery, who slew Henri II, King of France, accidentally, at a tournament in Paris in 1559; but there was no portrait of him at The Grove. The small dining-room was used for breakfast, which seldom started before 10 a.m. About twenty minutes later my uncle would appear. He never failed to convey to us, without saying so specifically, that he had been up and about for hours, dealing with his correspondence. We knew this to be quite untrue, but we kept our knowledge to ourselves. There was a small room beyond, into which guests never penetrated. My grand-father's official correspondence and papers were kept there behind a locked grille.

Judged by the standards of today, the domestic staff at The Grove was enormous, and there were many more servants than ever appeared. For instance, there were two men, somewhere in the background, whose sole duties were to fill and trim the colza-oil lamps—there was no electricity or gas laid on. In the foreground were the butler, my uncle's personal valet, and Mr Drowly, the groom of the chambers, a man of charm and exquisite manners, who remained in the service of the Clarendons from the age of fifteen until his death some years ago when he was seventy-five. At dinner he assisted the butler in keeping the wine-glasses full of champagne, and he was responsible for seeing that all the bedrooms, as well as the living-rooms, were plentifully supplied with thick cream-coloured note-paper of a kind unobtainable today, stamped in the right-hand top corner with the address, and in the left with an earl's coronet, both in light blue, as well as with pen-holders, each with a new gold nib, pencils, india-rubber, and every other writing requisite imaginable. What else he did, or was supposed to do, I never discovered. Then there were four 'figure' footmen in livery, each of them well over six feet tall. They must have had an uncommonly easy life, but I suppose they satisfied the needs of the numerous housemaids. In the kitchen there were at least four kitchen and scullery maids under the orders of Monsieur Thévenot, the French chef, and of his successor, Monsieur Menessier. They were both great artists. Well do I remember, and ardently, but in vain, do I long for *Homard Thévenot*: small pieces of hot lobster, cooked in *bouillon*, and covered with a mixture of yolk of egg, plenty of liqueur brandy and even more cream, Madeira, herbs, and M. Thévenot in his heavenly mansion alone knows what else besides. M. Menessier's *Macédoine de Faisan* was not to be despised—cuts from a pheasant's breast, immersed in a creamy yellow sauce, the basis of which was truffles and mushrooms. *Parfait de foie gras* was equally acceptable to a schoolboy entering on his 'teens. The *foie gras* from Strasburg was an annual Christmas present from my uncle's wine-merchant. I have an idea that in these degenerate days both donor and recipient could be haled before the Courts on charges of bribery and corruption.

Dinner was ceremonious. Full evening dress for the ladies, tail-coats, white waistcoats and white ties for the men—we boys, who did not possess such garments, were allowed to wear dinner jackets and black ties—and the four figure footmen in claret-coloured coats, dove-grey waistcoats, plush knee-breeches, silk stockings, and shoes with gold buckles. I do not think that in point of fact we over-ate. There was, of course, much more to eat than nowadays, and an infinitely greater variety of food ; but with three or four courses to follow, we took a smaller helping of fish than if, as so often happens now, fish were the one and only 'meat' course. The truth is that for the past ten years we have been, and still are, under-eating.

At the end of dinner, a footman brought round a superb William and Mary silver-gilt circular dish full of rosewater, in which we each dabbled our fingers in turn. Behind the footman hovered Mr Drowly, bearing an ewer matching the rosewater dish, in case the supply in the latter should run short. Some three or four years ago, shortly after her *début,* Princess Elizabeth, as she then was, and a number of her youthful friends and contemporaries, were entertained by the present Lord and Lady Clarendon at their residence in St. James's

Palace. At the end of dinner the rosewater dish appeared. None of the guests, including Her Royal Highness, had ever seen the like before, and asked what they were supposed to do.

There was one bathroom only, adjoining my uncle's bedroom and reserved for him alone. We had baths in our bedrooms. They were flat circular tubs, by the side of which stood two large cans of boiling water and one of cold, enamelled white and bearing the name of the bedroom in gold letters. I prefer a big bath, but there is a good deal to be said for a tub in front of a blazing fire.

On Boxing Day and the day after there were Christmas shoots for the boys. I must admit that as a rule they were not a great success. There was little to shoot, and my uncle was always in a rage. Regularly, at the end of every beat, he apostrophized the head-keeper in a loud and angry voice: 'Bamford, you're a fool.' 'Yes, m'lord,' replied Bamford with complete composure.

My first cousin, the present Lord Clarendon, sold The Grove about twenty years ago. During the war it was occupied by the clerical staff of one of the railway companies. In the spring of 1942 my sister, the late Mrs Harry Graham, had occasion to go to Watford. She suggested that I should take an afternoon off from the Ministry of Economic Warfare and accompany her, and that when she had finished her business in Watford we should go to The Grove and recall *les neiges d'antan*. I gladly agreed.

The stucco lodges on the London road looked unchanged. So did the park, except that no deer were browsing under the trees. The drive sloped as steeply as before down to the hump-backed stone bridges over the river and the canal, and up to the charming red brick house, looking just what an English country house ought to look like. We entered through an open french window into what was once the library. Office chairs and office desks, empty bookshelves, peeling paint, general squalor and dilapidation met our eyes. It was the same in the rest of that once noble suite of rooms. We found it inexpressibly painful, and we wished that we had never come. We stayed but a few minutes, and left in silence. There were tears in our eyes.

Though there have been many disasters at sea in two world wars there remains something peculiarly poignant about the greatest maritime tragedy that ever occurred in peace. And it is actually true that, as the Titanic *sank, her ship's band played 'Nearer, my God, to Thee'*

S.O.S. Titanic

by DEREK HUDSON

IT was Mr Lawrence Beesley's first trip across the Atlantic, and he was congratulating himself, that fourth day out from Southampton, on his good fortune in making such a smooth and pleasant voyage. Yes, emphatically it had been well worth while going on the largest ship afloat—46,000 tons, nearly 900 feet long, 75,000 pounds of fresh meat on board, not to mention the forty tons of potatoes, the 35,000 fresh eggs and the fifteen thousand bottles of ale and stout. . . . She was quite as comfortable as the advertisements had said ; and, behind all the luxury, the passengers had the soothing knowledge that she had been built for safety. The Captain could close the watertight bulkhead doors by 'simply moving an electric switch,' in the words of the owners' description, 'practically making the vessel unsinkable.' One could enjoy the Verandah Café, the Turkish Bath, the Gymnasium, the Parisian Café or the handsome library, just as if they were all part of a hotel on land. Such was life in 1912—astonishing! And they had made very good progress so far, an average of 22 knots, though they weren't racing. New York was only two days' steaming away, and Mr Beesley sat in the library that Sunday afternoon, April 14, 1912, contemplating a baggage declaration-form that the steward had given him : 'Form for non-residents in the United States. Steamship Titanic : No. 31444, D,' etc.

There was no sign, that Sunday afternoon, of the fulfilment of the 'bad omens' which had been so much discussed when the liner sailed. That this was the *Titanic's* maiden voyage had been enough, of itself, to upset many superstitious people. But she was also the sister-ship of the *Olympic,* which had lately been involved in a collision ; and as she left Southampton the *Titanic* herself had nearly collided with the *New York.* Something rather more macabre had happened at Queenstown, where an adventurous stoker had climbed up inside one of the huge funnels—a dummy one used for ventilation—and showed his black face at the top, to the consternation of a number of passengers who were being brought out to the *Titanic* in a tender, and who accepted the apparition as a portent of disaster. What foolishness! thought Mr Beesley—but it was the sort of nonsense that disturbed confidence, however slightly, and made the atmosphere rather less healthy than it ought to have been.

Yet to Mr Beesley himself, and to most of the 2,200 people on board, the *Titanic* seemed quite as 'unsinkable' as the advertisements suggested. 'Truly she was a magnificent boat!' And you got an extraordinary impression of her size by taking the lift from the top and dropping slowly down past the different floors, discharging and receiving passengers just like in a hotel. The lift-boy was a jolly lad, about sixteen, with a great love of the sea—which, while he was on duty, he hardly ever saw. Once, when he put Mr Beesley out of the lift, he noticed a game of deck quoits in progress through the vestibule windows and said wistfully, 'My! I wish I could go out there sometimes!' Mr Beesley jokingly offered to take charge of the lift while he watched the game, 'but he smilingly shook his head and dropped down in answer to an imperative ring from below.'

Little did Mr Beesley think that this Sunday, forty years ago, was to be the last day in the life of that boy ; or of the robust and energetic gym instructor, another of his friends ; or of so many more of the men and women who were his companions. Nor could he have dreamed that only a few months later he would be holding in his hands his own well-written and most moving book, *The Loss of the R.M.S. Titanic: Its Story and Its Lessons.*

*　　*　　*　　*　　*

Already, however, at 9 a.m. on that fatal Sunday, a wireless message from the *Caronia* had been received by Captain E. C. Smith which might have made his passengers, if they had known of it, think twice about the particularly chilly wind on deck that morning. It read as follows : 'Captain, "Titanic."—West-bound steamers report bergs growlers and field-ice in 42° N. from 49° to 51° W., 12th April. Compliments.—Barr.' And at 1.42 p.m. there was another message, this time from the *Baltic,* which said: 'Greek steamer "Athenai" reports passing icebergs and large quantities of field ice today in lat. 41° 51′ N. long. 49° 52′ W. . . . Wish you and "Titanic" all success.—Commander.' Captain Smith showed this message to Mr Bruce Ismay, the managing director of the White Star Line, who was one of his passengers, and Mr Ismay understood from the message that they 'would get up to the ice that night.'

Three further warnings of ice were received by the *Titanic* in the course of the day. The last and most serious reached the Marconi room at 9.40 p.m., while Mr Beesley and several hundred other people were singing hymns in the saloon at the invitation of Mr Carter, a clergyman. Among the hymns were 'For those in peril on the Sea.' The singing went on until after ten o'clock, when Mr Carter thanked the purser for the use of the saloon and expressed the confidence of the passengers in the *Titanic* and their gratitude for a pleasant voyage. Then, after eating biscuits and drinking coffee, most of those who had taken part went to bed.

Meanwhile, the latest wireless message that might have saved so many lives lay disregarded on the operator's table. It was from a steamer called the *Mesaba:*

'From "Mesaba" to "Titanic" and all east-bound ships. Ice report in lat. 42° N. to 41° 25′ N, long. 49° to long. 50° 30′ W. Saw much heavy pack ice and great number large icebergs. Also field ice. Weather good, clear.'

In the words of Lord Mersey, in his official report on the loss of the *Titanic,* 'This message clearly indicated the presence of ice in the immediate vicinity of the "Titanic," and if it had reached the bridge would perhaps have affected the navigation of the vessel. Unfortunately, it does not appear to have been delivered to the Master or to any of the officers. The Marconi operator was very busy from 8 o'clock onward transmitting messages via Cape Race for passengers on board the "Titanic," and the probability is that he failed to grasp the significance and importance of the message, and put it aside until he should be less busy. It was never acknowledged by Captain Smith, and I am satisfied that it was not received by him.'

Nevertheless, the Captain had already received ample warning that the *Titanic* was approaching the region of the ice. He had had a talk about it with the Second Officer Mr Lightoller at nine o'clock, and when he went to his room at 9.30 his parting remark was : 'If it becomes at all doubtful, let me know at once ; I will be just inside.' And as soon as Captain Smith had retired Mr Lightoller sent a message to the crow's nest 'to keep a sharp look-out for ice' until daylight. Yet it remains a fact that the Captain did not take either of the two precautionary measures open to him—to stand well to the southward, or to reduce speed considerably as night approached.

To Mr Beesley, who had gone to bed, it even seemed that they were actually travelling faster than at any time since they had left Queenstown. When he sat on his sofa undressing, with his bare feet on the floor, 'the jar of the vibration came up from the engines below very noticeably,' and when he sat up in his berth reading, 'the spring mattress supporting me was vibrating more rapidly than usual.' In fact, however, at 10 p.m. the ship was registering only a little, if any, more than the same high rate which had been kept up throughout the voyage ; and the Official Report accepts the speed at the time of the collision as about 22 knots.

At 11.40 p.m. one of the look-outs in the crow's-nest struck three blows on the gong, which was the accepted warning for something ahead, and telephoned to the bridge 'Iceberg right ahead.' Mr Murdoch, the officer of the watch, gave the order 'Hard-a-starboard' and telegraphed down to the engine-room: 'Stop. Full speed astern.' The helm was already 'hard over,' and the ship's head had fallen off about two points to port, when the *Titanic* collided with an iceberg well forward on her starboard side.

At that moment Mr Murdoch pulled the lever which closed the water-tight doors in the engine and boiler rooms. Captain Smith 'rushed out' on to the bridge and asked him what the ship had struck. 'An iceberg, Sir,' replied Mr Murdoch. 'I hard-a-starboarded and reversed the engines, and I was going to hard-a-port round it but she was too close. I could not do any more. I have closed the water-tight doors.'

*   *   *   *   *

The jar was apparently not much felt on board. Mr Lightoller, who was in his cabin, described it as 'a slight grinding, and then a shock, with very little noise.' Mr Beesley, lower down in the ship, felt only 'an extra heave of the engines and a more than usually obvious dancing motion of the mattress on which I sat.' There was no heavy jolt or list to port—and yet the *Titanic's* plates had been cut like butter and water was pouring through her side. Mr Beesley put on his shoes and dressing-gown and climbed three flights of stairs to the top deck, more out of the curiosity of an inexperienced traveller than from any sense of alarm. It was icy cold ; the engines had stopped and the ship was stationary ; many feet below, the sea lay calm and black ; but there was nothing to suggest that anything serious had happened.

In the smoking-room a passenger who was playing cards said he had seen a huge iceberg go by. He and his friends thought the *Titanic* must have struck it a glancing blow and that they had stopped as a precaution. 'I expect the iceberg has scratched off some of her new paint,' said one of them, 'and the Captain doesn't like to go on until she is painted up again.' Another player pointed to the glass of whisky beside him and, turning to an onlooker, said: 'Just run along the deck and see if any ice has come aboard : I would like some for this.' He spoke truer than he knew, for the forward deck was then covered with ice that had toppled over during the collision.

Mr Beesley decided to return to his cabin. Before he left the deck, he saw an officer climb on to a lifeboat and begin to throw off the cover—but the significance of this did not occur to him. He did, however, notice that the ship now had a slight tilt forward, and he felt something unusual about the stairs as he went down, 'a curious sense of something out of balance and of not being able to put one's foot down in the right place.'

Very few people on board realized then that the ship was doomed, or knew that in the first ten minutes water had filled the five forward compartments to a height of about 14 feet above the keel. If the flooding could have been confined to three or even four compartments, the *Titanic* might have remained afloat ; but, as it was, she had no chance.

Captain Smith went straight to the wireless cabin, where Harold Bride, the second operator, was about to relieve the chief operator, Jack Phillips. 'We've struck an iceberg,' he said, 'and I'm having an inspection made to tell what it's done to us. You'd better get ready to send out a call for assistance ; but don't send it until I tell you.' Ten minutes later he came back and ordered, 'Send a call for assistance,' barely putting his head round the door. Phillips began by sending the old signal, 'C.Q.D,' but later, at Bride's suggestion, changed to what was then the new signal, the 'S.O.S.' Bride told him that it might be his last chance to send it, and at this they both laughed.

The messages between the *Titanic* and the many ships that answered her during the next two hours tell their own moving story. She was early in touch with the Cunarder *Carpathia,* fifty-eight miles away, who at once turned north to the rescue. At 12.26 Phillips says : 'Can hear nothing for noise of steam,' and at 1.10 a.m. he tells the *Olympic* 'Sinking head down. Get your boats ready.' At 1.25 *Titanic* says : 'We are putting the women off in the boats,' and at 1.35 ' Engine room getting flooded,' Soon afterwards the *Baltic* tells *Titanic,* 'We are rushing to you,' and the *Olympic* says, 'Am lighting up all possible boilers as fast as can.' The last signals from the *Titanic* are heard by the *Carpathia* at 1.45 a.m.: 'Engine-room full up to boilers.'

* * * * *

'All passengers on deck with lifebelts on !' The cry had brought everyone out of their cabins ; but the *Titanic* still seemed so solid and safe that there was hardly any alarm among the passengers. Only the deafening boom of steam escaping from a pipe high up in one of the funnels caused some disquiet, and made conversation difficult. The crowd watched the crew at work on the lifeboats, arranging oars, coiling ropes, testing the davits. An officer came along the boat deck and shouted above the noise : 'All women and children get down to deck below and all men stand back from the boats.' It was the first hint of imminent danger ; but discipline held ; the order was obeyed. And then, dramatically, came an ominous sign that confirmed the worst fears. As Mr Beesley says, 'Suddenly a rush of light from the forward deck, a hissing roar that made us all turn from watching the boats, and a rocket leapt upwards to where the stars blinked and twinkled above us. Up it went, higher and higher, with a sea of faces upturned to watch it, and then an explosion that seemed to split the silent night in two, and a shower of stars sank slowly down and went out one by one. And with a gasping sigh one word escaped the lips of the crowd : 'Rockets!'

Eight rockets were fired. It is a tragic feature of the disaster that these rockets were seen from the steamer *Californian,* which was lying surrounded by loose ice no more than eight or ten miles away. She could have pushed her way through the ice to open water without any serious risk and might have saved many if not all the lives that were lost. But the *Californian's* wireless operator was off duty, and though her second officer was heard to say 'A ship is not going to fire rockets at sea for nothing,' by a succession of accidents, bordering on negligence, no action was taken.

The all too few boats on the *Titanic* were filled and lowered. But only 652 people went into those boats which had accommodation for 1,178. It was faulty organization rather than bad discipline that was to blame. And many men who might have been saved in them were turned away while the cry was for 'Women and children only.'

The boats stood out from the *Titanic* and watched her as, with her lights still blazing, she settled lower and lower in the water. Crew and passengers alike did their duty bravely. The wireless operators stayed at their post. The ship's band, on the deck, played 'Nearer, my God, to Thee.' Shortly after 2 a.m. she slowly tilted straight on end with the stern vertically upwards, and the machinery roared down through the vessel with a groaning rattle. At 2.20 a.m. the *Titanic* disappeared—and, to the horror of those in the boats, there arose the appalling cries of hundreds of people thrown into the icy water.

The last glimpse of Captain Smith is a noble one. He had encouraged them all to the end and was on the bridge when the *Titanic* went down. Then he swam with a child to one of the boats and saw it to safety. 'What became of Murdoch (the first officer)?' he asked. When someone answered that he was dead, 'the captain released his grasp of the gunwale and slowly sank before our eyes.'

Of those that went down with the ship, only sixty were saved. Joining those already in the boats, they made a total of 712 that were rescued by the *Carpathia* an hour or two later. The remainder, nearly 1,500, were lost. They included many poor people, and many wealthy and eminent people, among the latter a famous journalist, W. T. Stead.

* * * * *

In considering this greatest of all maritime disasters, it is important not to throw undue blame on unfortunate Captain Smith, who to the last behaved so gallantly and well. Why did he persevere in his course and maintain his speed, when others perhaps—and especially those wise after the event—would have done neither? The answer, as Lord Mersey pointed out in his report, lay in the practice of liners using the accepted Outward Southern Track for the previous quarter of a century. When in the vicinity of ice at night, in clear weather, they had kept to the course, maintained speed, and trusted to a sharp look-out to avoid danger.

The agreed track followed by the *Titanic* passed about 25 miles south of an area marked on the chart 'Field ice between March and July,' but was well inside another area marked 'Icebergs have been seen within this line in April, May and June.' Some risk was, therefore, recognized ; but as there had been no casualties in the past, the practice had been continued. Its root, as Lord Mersey said, was probably to be found in the competition between the different shipping companies and the public desire for quick crossings. But Captain Smith had not been urged to make a particularly rapid crossing on this occasion ; he had complete discretion, as usual, to do what he thought best. In Lord Mersey's words, 'He made a mistake, a very grievous mistake, but one in which, in view of the practice and of past experience, negligence cannot be said to have had any part, and in the absence of negligence it is, in my opinion, impossible to fix Captain Smith with blame.' But Lord Mersey did take care to add : 'What was a mistake in the case of the "Titanic" would without doubt be negligence in any similar case in future.'

Could such a disaster happen today? The answer is that the risk

has been very greatly reduced. To begin with, there are now agreed
North Atlantic tracks for different times of the year, arranged according to the ice movements. There is also an organized international ice
patrol, which did not exist in 1912. Again, radio was then in its
infancy, and vast progress has since been made in radio direction-
finding, in radio-communication, and in radar.

After the Board of Trade enquiry into the loss of the *Titanic,* the
regulations were amended so as to increase the number of lifeboats
in passenger liners. In the majority of passenger liners today, there
is a place in a boat for everyone on board ; that is laid down in an
appendix to the Merchant Shipping Act (there is an exception in the
case of ships built before 1925, but they must provide alternative life-
saving equipment). The full complement of the *Queen Mary* is about
3,100, and she carries—beside a number of life-rafts—24 power-driven
lifeboats with a total capacity of more than 3,200.

Joseph Conrad, who could be a ranting jingo when he took to
journalism, wrote a couple of angry magazine articles about the loss
of the *Titanic*—one of the things that annoyed him most was that there
had not been any motor-engines in the boats. And he went on : " I,
who am not a sentimentalist, think it would have been finer if the band
of the *Titanic* had been quietly saved, instead of being drowned while
playing—whatever tune they were playing, the poor devils. I would
rather they had been saved to support their families than see their
families supported by the magnificent generosity of the subscribers.
I am not consoled by the false, written-up Drury Lane aspects of
that event, which is neither drama, nor melodrama, nor tragedy, but
the exposure of arrogant folly. There is nothing more heroic in being
drowned very much against your will, off a holed, helpless, big tank
in which you bought your passage, than in dying of colic caused by the
imperfect salmon in the tin you bought from your grocer. . . .'

This sarcastic rhetoric was not worthy of Conrad, who knew, as well
as you or I know, that there was not only drama, but also melodrama,
tragedy and heroism in the sinking of the *Titanic*. But his concern
was genuine. He wished above all that the lesson should be heeded,
and that such a disaster should never be possible again. Those lives
lost forty years ago remind us that the price of safety at sea, like that
of liberty itself, is still 'eternal vigilance.'

An Anthology of Insects

with wood-engravings by

ERIC FITCH DAGLISH

THE BEE

Fly to my mistress, pretty pilfering bee,
And say, thou bring'st this honey-bag from me:
When on her lip thou hast thy sweet dew placed,
Mark if her tongue but slyly steal a taste.
If so, we live; if not, with mournful hum,
Toll forth my death; next, to my burial come.

ROBERT HERRICK (1591–1674)

I took the honey from the bee;
On the bag these words were seen:
'More sweet than this
Perchance naught is,
Yet gall it might have been:
If God it should so please,
He could still make it such with ease;
And as will gall to honey change can He';'
This learned I of the bee.

PATRICK CAREY (*c*. 1651)

D

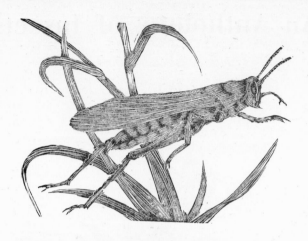

THE GRASSHOPPER AND THE CRICKET

Green little vaulter in the sunny grass,
Catching your heart up at the feel of June,
Sole voice that's heard amidst the lazy noon,
When even the bees lag at the summoning brass,
And you, warm little housekeeper, who class
With those who think the candles come too soon,
Loving the fire, and with your tricksome tune
Nick the glad silent moments as they pass :
Oh sweet and tiny cousins that belong
One to the fields, the other to the hearth,
Both have your sunshine ; both, though small, are strong
At your clear hearts ; and both seem given to earth
To ring in thoughtful ears this natural song—
Indoors and out, summer and winter, Mirth.

LEIGH HUNT (1784–1859)

THE FLEA

Lady, the silly flea of all disdained
    Because it hath complained,
    I pity that poor creature,
    Both black and small of stature.
Were I a flea in bed I would not bite you,
But search some other way for to delight you.

GILES FARNABY (fl 1598)

THE BEE-WISP

Our window-panes enthral our summer bees;
(To insect woes I give this little page)—
We hear them threshing in their idle rage
Those crystal floors of famine, while, at ease,
Their outdoor comrades probe the nectaries
Of flowers, and into all sweet blossoms dive;
Then home, at sundown, to the happy hive,
On forward wing, straight through the dancing flies:
For such poor strays a full-plumed wisp I keep,
And when I see them pining, worn, and vext,
I brush them softly with a downward sweep
To the raised sash—all-anger'd and perplext:
So man, the insect, stands on his defence
Against the very hand of Providence.

CHARLES TENNYSON TURNER (1808–1879)

MITES

Dear madam, did you never gaze,
Through optic-glass, on rotten cheese?
There, madam, did you ne'er perceive
A crowd of dwarfish creatures live?
The little things, elate with pride,
Strut to and fro, from side to side:
In tiny pomp, and pertly vain,
Lords of their pleasing orb, they reign;
And, fill'd with harden'd curds and cream,
Think the whole dairy made for *them*.

So men, conceited lords of all,
Walk proudly o'er this pendant ball,
Fond of their little spot below,
Nor greater beings care to know;
But think those worlds, which deck the skies,
Were only form'd to please *their* eyes.

THE REV. STEPHEN DUCK (1705–1756)

THE DRAGON FLY

Now, when my roses are half buds, half flowers,
    And loveliest, the king of flies has come—
It was a fleeting visit, all too brief ;
    In three short minutes he had seen them all,
And rested, too, upon an apple leaf.

There, his round shoulders humped with emeralds,
    A gorgeous opal crown set on his head,
And all those shining honours to his breast—
    'My garden is a lovely place,' thought I,
'But is it worthy of so fine a guest?'

He rested there, upon that apple leaf—
    'See, see,' I cried amazed, 'His opal crown,
And all those emeralds clustered round his head!'
    'His breast, my dear, how lovely was his breast'—
The voice of my Beloved quickly said.

'See, see his gorgeous crown, that shines
    With all those jewels bulging round its rim'—
I cried aloud at night, in broken rest.
    Back came the answer quickly, in my dream—
'His breast, my dear, how lovely was his breast!'

W. H. DAVIES (1871–1940)

THE BUTTERFLY

Like as the divers-freckled butterfly
When winter's frost is fall'n upon his wing,
Hath only left life's possibility,
And lies half dead until the cheerful spring :

But then the Sun from his all-quick'ning eye
Darts forth a sparkle of the living fire
Which with kind heat doth warm the frozen fly
And with new spirit his little breast inspire :

Then doth he lightly rise and spread his wings
And with the beams that gave him life doth play :
Tastes every flower that on the earth's bosom springs,
And is in busy motion all the day.

SIR JOHN DAVIES (1569–1626)

Child of the sun! pursue thy rapturous flight,
Mingling with her thou lov'st in fields of light ;
And, where the flowers of paradise unfold,
Quaff fragrant nectar from their cups of gold.
There shall thy wings, rich as an evening sky,
Expand and shut with silent ecstasy !
—Yet wert thou once a worm, a thing that crept
On the bare earth, then wrought a tomb and slept.
And such is man ; soon from his cell of clay
To burst a seraph in the blaze of day !

SAMUEL ROGERS (1763–1855)

85

THE SILKWORM

Hence, when the morn's in Italy's lands,
To spring's warm beam its timid leaf expands ;
The silk-worm broods in countless tribes above
Crop the green treasure, uniformed of love ;
Erewhile the changeful worm, with circling head
Weaves the nice curtains of his silken bed ;
Web within web involves his larva form,
Alike secured from sunshine and from storm ;
For twelve long days he dreams of blossomed groves,
Untasted honey and ideal loves ;
Wakes from his trance, alarmed with young desire,
Finds his new sex, and feels ecstatic fire ;
From flower to flower, with honeyed lip he springs,
And seeks his velvet loves on silver wings.

ERASMUS DARWIN (1731–1802)

THE FLY

Once musing as I sat,
　　and candle burning by,
When all were hushed I might discern
　　a simple silly fly,
That flew before mine eyes,
　　with free rejoicing heart,
and here and there, with wings did play
　　as void of pain and smart.
Sometime by me she sat,
　　when she had played her fill,
And ever when she rested had
　　about she fluttered still.
When I perceived her well,
　　rejoicing in her place,
O happy fly, quoth I, and eake,
　　O worm in happy case.
Which two of us is best?
　　I that have reason? no :
But thou that reason art without
　　and therewith void of woe.
I live and so dost thou,
　　but I live all in pain,
And subject am to her alas,
　　that makes my grief her gain.

BARNABE GOOGE (1540-1594)

The World of Arthur Devis

by SACHEVERELL SITWELL

ARTHUR DEVIS (1711–87) is one of the two or three masters of the English Conversation Piece. He came from Preston, in Lancashire, where he narrowly escaped serious trouble during the '45 Rebellion because of his close personal likeness to the Young Pretender. Arthur Devis perhaps had lessons from Pieter Tillemans (1684–1734), an Antwerp painter of Conversation Pieces who worked in the North of England and East Anglia. Little enough is known of Arthur Devis, except that he lived at 66, Great Queen Street, Lincoln's Inn Fields, died at Brighton, and that there were other painters of his family.

So we can come directly to his pictures. These are among the delights of the eighteenth century in England. Once seen, his is a style which quickly becomes familiar, though, mistakenly, too many paintings with stiff, wooden figures are attributed to him. Perhaps the best place to get acquainted with his delightful mannerisms is at Uppark, Sussex, where eight pictures of single figures, all in gilded Chippendale frames, hang together in a cluster on the staircase wall. There, if you have not met with him before, you may feel you are in the presence of the English equivalent to Pietro Longhi. But that Venetian painter, seldom, if ever, sets foot upon the *terra firma*. His themes are the boudoir and the gambling hell. Devis, at Uppark, reminds you of Longhi, but only so long as you are looking for a name. Once in possession of that, another and new personality begins to form. In single figures, and small canvases, as at Uppark, Devis is naïf, and then he is like Longhi, if you forget the Venetian *bauta* (bird-mask) and black domino. Devis has a lighter hand than Hogarth, who never failed to communicate his bigness to his paintings. A small Hogarth never delights because it is so little. But Devis builds up from his initial smallness. He does not contract in order to be small. He expands as his hand gets surer. And of course the great difference between this Lancashire painter and Longhi, who was contemporary to him (1702–64), is that his stiffness vanishes when his subjects pose for him, not in their George II interiors, but out of doors. This is where he is English. His patrons, as one would expect, seem to have been county families. He exhibited at the Free Society of Artists, in London ; and the miniature lay figure used by him for painting is now in the Art Gallery at his native Preston.

MR AND MRS STARKIE   *Robert Tritton, Esq.*

A MUSICAL party out of doors, with a patient listener. No doubt
Mr Starkie, Mayor of Preston in 1754, engaged in the same
pastime during winter evenings. In the distance is Hoghton
Tower ; a Palladian gazebo shows behind the tree. (30 × 25 ins.)

WO scions of ancient Lancastrian families in a romantic Northern
landscape in 1743.   Preston, where Devis then lived, had
long association with the Jacobites.   In the '15, the Chevalier St
George (Old Pretender) raised his standard at the market cross.
In the '45 the young Chevalier was proclaimed King in the market
place, but passed through again, soon after, on his retreat from Derby.
So Preston often saw the Jacobite officers, 'in laced hats with white
cockades, and scotch plaid sashes lined with white ribband, drums
beating, and pipes (bagpipes) playing,' as reported in *State Trials*.
The Jacobites 'fell victims to the hospitality of the Preston inhabitants
and the smiles of the Lancashire witches.'   One of them says 'the
Ladys in this town are so very beautiful and so richly attired, that the
gentlemen soldiers from Wednesday to Saturday minded nothing but
courting and feasting.'   But Dr Whitaker calls Preston, peevishly,
'an elegant and economical town, the resort of well born, but ill por-
tioned and ill endowed, old maids and widows.'   (29 × 36½ ins.)

THE JAMES FAMILY   *The Tate Gallery*

DEVIS at his most elegant. The grass is like a 'stage' carpet, and the picture is beautifully composed. Note the superb stone garden-vase to the right, which 'ties in' the figures, according to a device well known to scene-painters ; for example, the two wings painted with still-lives in Derain's setting for *La Boutique Fantasque*. Those fulfil the same purpose. The lake enlivens the landscape ; and at the far end there is a fine Palladian pavilion or boat-house in the style of William Kent. Where was this country house ; and what is left of it? Is it Upminster Hall, Essex, near Tilbury? All must have been brand new in 1751 when this painting was signed and dated. Note, also, the garden chairs of most elegant design. The James family, too, are as though wearing brand new dresses. Mr Robert James, *tricorne* in hand, wears a handsome waistcoat; the hooped skirts of the ladies of the family, diminishing in order of age, are not the least delight of this picture. The parents are divided, theatrically, from their children in order to show the lake. (38¾ × 49 ins.)

THE ROOKES LEEDS FAMILY *Major and the Hon. Mrs Macdonald-Buchanan*

PROBABLY the masterpiece of the painter, its only flaw being the ugly aunt in a blue dress in the background. A Yorkshire landscape, at Royds Hall, with a few clouds in the sky, a winding river, and distant view (of Bradford?). Under a tree, on a painted garden seat of good and sensible design, sit two ladies. Their silken dresses are beautifully painted; as are all the details, the sun bonnet on the seat beside the younger woman, and the blue bag on the arm of the older woman in oyster satin, who appears to be engaged in polishing her fingernails. Mr Edward Rookes Leeds stands apart and regards his family. On the right, a lady in pale brown brocaded with silver, plays a mandoline. One would like to know the secret of the posing of these outdoor paintings. The Rookes Leeds family, all middle-aged, must have been an easier problem than the Bertie family (opposite). Perhaps the foliage of the trees is a little indeterminate; and in both paintings the grass at their feet could be a 'stage' carpet put down in lengths. (40 × 50 ins.)

Viscount Wimborne

A LOVELY, 'flowing' composition, natural and easy in grouping. The landscape stands out, clearly, and carefully considered, with a lake and distant hills behind the figure of the Duke, who is given importance standing by himself, gun under arm. For the rest of the composition, grouped in two sets of threes, there is a dark wooded background against which they stand out in detail. The centre group of two young ladies gives the colour to this outdoor Conversation Piece. Remark the pale blue silk dress and the blue sun bonnet held in the left hand. Behind her, her companion in a white silk hooped skirt wears a black sprigged bodice, almost like a mantilla. The young boy in the right-hand group is in riding clothes like those worn in Wootton's huge hunting groups at Longleat and Badminton. He wears a black 'montero' hunting cap, of the type that came into England in the reign of Charles II. His sister's *café au lait* dress is lightened by the blue sun bonnet in her right hand. Painted about 1745. (40 × 50 ins.)

THE LOVE SONG

E. E. Cook, Esq.

A COOL interior, lit by a Palladian window, and enlivened by pleasing landscapes upon the wall. A bare room, kept free for music, probably an 'end room,' in one of a pair of pavilions at each end of the house. We may amuse ourselves planning an imaginary tour of the rest of it. Should, perhaps, be called *The Sonata,* not *The Love Song.* Signed and dated 1749. (44 × 40 ins.)

HE REV. STREYNSHAM MASTER AND HIS WIFE *Sir Brian Mountain*

THIS time a Lancashire interior, and a charmingly formal arrangement and composition. The clergyman and his wife are moored in front of us upon the raft-like carpet. The portraits, on the wall at the back, are Streynsham Master's brother and sister, making it a composition of four persons on two storeys. It is a flowered carpet, the clergyman and his wife hold flowers in their hands ; and there are flowers on the table, and flowers have dropped upon the floor. Through the window of the room beyond there is a view of Croston Church. All is so meticulously in place that you may fancy you hear the clock ticking. The 'divine,' with white lappet, is dressed in sober black, and wears a short 'tie-wig.' There is the feeling that it is a cool spring evening ; we would know the month if only we could see those flowers in detail. The further room seems filled with the golden light of sunset. But nothing moves. And, taking our eyes from those four portraits, the stereoscopic vision of that spring evening fades away. (33 × 40 ins.)

THE THOMLINSON FAMILY   *Arthur Tooth and Sons*

THE THOMLINSONS were a Cumberland family, from 'The Hill,' near Carlisle. This is one more of Devis's 'raft' or 'magic carpet' paintings. Mr John Thomlinson 'in command' and seated, authoritatively, at a table. Next to him, hands on lap, is his wife, resigned for a long sitting. Miss Bourke, in pink, stands by her. Miss Grainger, in pale blue, sits, book in hand, but obviously in no mood for reading. Master Thomlinson holds a closed book in his hand and is, perhaps, reciting to make time pass quicker. A sturdy sea-picture hangs over the fireplace, and the vessel flies a large flag. Is it a merchant ship of Mr Thomlinson's? The geographical globe supports this theory. And, perhaps, the Turkey carpet. A splendid Palladian or 'Venetian' window looks out on to a park. A window of this kind cannot have been built more than twenty or twenty-five years before the date of the painting, signed and dated 1745. The figures are a little doll-like and tight in handling. They are not as 'realized' as the Rev. Streynsham Master and his wife, and the picture is not so successful as a peepshow. Were there, really, as many Palladian windows in the countryside? This specimen is almost identical with that in *The Love Song*. Did Devis sketch his patrons in their homes, and complete his paintings in his London studio? ($23\frac{3}{4} \times 39\frac{3}{4}$ ins.)

THE stature of Devis grows perceptibly in looking at him. It is a considerable painter who achieved the *James Family.* That is perhaps as good a Conversation in a landscape as one would expect of him ; just as the *Rev. Streynsham Master and his Wife* is the best of his interiors. The quality of the latter picture is still its naïveté or quaintness ; in the sense that many eighteenth-century English tomb sculptures, now beginning to be appreciated at their worth, 'amuse,' because of the wigs and armour, and long inscriptions in fine letters. But Devis could do better. His paintings of *Edward Rookes Leeds and Family,* and the *Duke of Ancaster and Family,* are an unexpected improvement upon himself. There is nothing puppet-like about the figures, which fill their places in the composition as though by instinct. Perhaps in the Rookes Leeds group a French painter would have made more play of the four ladies' dresses. But, then, the scene is in Yorkshire and they are not Frenchwomen. He had to paint their dresses as he found them, and they are no product of Parisian dressmakers. Incidentally, in Devis there is no sign of French influence. He appears to be entirely ignorant of Watteau's paintings. Lancret, Pater, Boucher, were unknown to him ; or he has looked at them, and turned away. His old masters and examples were the minor Dutchmen, and not the Dutch masters whom we admire today. His initial awkwardness in his early pictures may be not so much due to naïveté as to the lack of models upon whom to form a style. Pieter Tillemans and 'Old' Nollekens (another Ant- werp painter (1702–48) and father of the sculptor), both Flemings, were virtual inventors of the English Conversation Piece, but it was a small thing, of few possibilities, in their hands. 'Old' Nollekens painted one delightful picture, *The Music Party* (Coll. Captain E. G. Spencer Churchill), where the figures are grouped outside Wanstead House, the home of Lord Tilney, but I think it is untrue to say this painting shows the influence of Watteau. *The Music Party,* it seems to me, is in the manner of Cornelis Troost (1697–1750), whose paintings and gouache drawings the Fleming may have seen on visits to The Hague and Amsterdam. But there is never an influence of Cornelis Troost in Devis. He can never, I surmise, have seen that Dutchman's pictures. In thinking of Devis we must establish it in our minds that the Con- versation Piece was something new. He had no forerunner or antecedent to help him. Hogarth was attempting the same thing ; but, in his whole career, Hogarth painted, perhaps, less than a dozen Conversation Pieces. Devis had to make slow progress, improving as he went along. Now, we look at him as an old painter. But, in his own eyes, he was new as the best clothes of his sitters. And he painted them in new and up to date surroundings, upon occasion, it is my theory, adding a Palladian window where there was none. There are geographical globes in two of the paintings that we illustrate. Was this a studio ' property'? Devis and Zoffany are the masters of the English Conversation Piece. Of the two, Devis belongs to the earlier and better period. He is the painter of country life in the lesser Georgian houses which are found all over England, and, with poverty descending on them, seem, now, like relics from a golden age.

SATURDAY BOOK STORIES

by YVONNE SEAGER

Illustrated by Brian Robb

L ENARITA'S sisters and cousins married ordinary people. Not exactly butchers and bakers and candlestick-makers, but ordinary people—doctors and schoolmasters and borough surveyors, anyway. Lenarita married George, but Lenarita had been a handful as a child.

She had long, pale hair that wasn't quite straight and wasn't really wavy. It shone wondrously if she polished it with an old silk handkerchief, after brushing. She had violet eyes, colour of stewed plums —the fruit, not the juice—and slim hands that could cook or model a new nail varnish, as the occasion required. She was left-handed, and superstitious, and insisted on believing in Father Christmas. She laughed or cried whenever she felt like it, which was often. (Her laughter was never jarring and her tears weren't messy, like most women's.) And she had the loveliest legs in Croydon, where she grew up. But she married George.

No one could possibly object to George himself. He was an intelligent, charming and highly original young man, and he looked reassuringly ordinary, as Lenny pointed out, when her family questioned her wisdom. George was polite to her parents, generous to her sisters and patient with her aunts. He didn't drink, wasn't paying alimony to another woman, and he adored her. Also he earned good money—so good that even without Lenny's rather fitful modelling they'd have enough presently for that house in the country, and the three pairs of twins they planned. Thanks to Waldo.

'George is a nice young fellow,' her father pointed out, 'but you know Waldo is your real breadwinner, Lenny.'

'Won't you meet some awful people, gipsies, for instance?' asked her eldest sister (married to a doctor in Croydon).

'Are you really sure you'll be happy with George?' her mother persisted. Her mother rather favoured Hobson Clark—he was so well off, so generous, and so amusing—and older, certainly. But of course love was the only thing that mattered, as she learned from the magazines she devoured under the drier at the hairdressers.

'I shall be very happy with George—and Waldo,' Lenny assured her. 'And I shan't have any forms to fill up like poor Daphne!' (Her second sister had married a hotel-keeper in Purley.)

Naturally, Lenny reasoned, her family couldn't be expected to take to Waldo overnight—they'd never met a Waldo before. Her father insisted it was a queer, undignified job for George, and her mother worried (unnecessarily) if it were ever dangerous. Her cousins made it clear they thought it was a social comedown, in spite of the money, and her kid brother Jack thought it was the best thing that had ever happened in the family.

Lenny looked like a princess at her wedding—one of the firms she'd modelled for did the gown, just for the advertisement. She was slim enough to wear an overskirt of jewelled net on white satin. It was a dateless sort of dress, and her head-dress was adapted from the fourteenth century, so she wouldn't have to look at her photographs in ten or twenty years' time and gasp, or giggle.

Waldo was the star at the reception, but Lenny didn't mind. Obviously he was terribly proud and happy, and anyone might have got excited and eaten too many sardine sandwiches, mightn't they? Even Hob made a fuss of him, and George and Lenny had their wedding photograph (the one they were going to show their grandchildren) with Waldo grinning between them. He wore a waistcoat with a carnation like the ushers, and played most of *Here Comes The Bride* on his pipes, instead of the National Anthem. Then Hob gave him some champagne, and started him sneezing.

'Gesundheit!' exclaimed Lenny's father automatically, and Waldo looked at him and winked.

George and Lenny found a tiny house in a mews. Of course, they couldn't have Waldo in a block of flats, so they found four tiny rooms over a garage that was big enough for Waldo's special travelling van and Lenny's bicycle. Waldo had the largest room made over to him, and the chauffeurs in the mews used to bring their children to watch him sunbathing on his tiny balcony. George taught Lenny how to look after him, for his needs were simple and he was fed by contract. Lenny even got back to eating fish herself after the first year.

They gave some highly successful parties in the three remaining rooms, and Waldo, who loved company, always insisted on joining in.

Sometimes George and Waldo had engagements out of town, and Lenny stayed behind and played hostess to her mother and sisters, and distributed the complimentary tickets Waldo always got to her nephews and nieces and their friends. Sometimes she went to watch Waldo and George in action, and once a man in the next seat asked for her autograph. George and Waldo even made trips abroad occasionally, and earned hard currency, and nylons for Lenny and her sisters. Lenny, not to be outdone, rose early, and plaiting and curling her long mane as directed, posed and postured in front of fashion cameras in slinky gowns that only fat old women who couldn't wear them could afford to buy. Then she, too, could wave a pay cheque at the returning travellers.

George and Lenny were very happy together. Every absence of George's successfully survived, and every safe return rapturously celebrated, seemed to bring them closer together. George and Lenny and Waldo, that is.

Naturally, Lenny had had various boy friends before George. Ever since she was eight to be exact. Any girl with Lenny's looks and ebullience always does. But since meeting George (at nineteen) and marrying him (not till twenty-one, as her father insisted) they had been so many names in the telephone directory. She never thought about them—except Hobson Clark.

When Lenny was eleven, she'd wandered into a Fun Fair, out of curiosity, and when the manager saw her unaccompanied, he'd chased her rather rudely out. Hobson Clark, who happened to be standing by, intervened.

'Let the kid alone,' he ordered. 'I'll look after her. You've been monkeying with your rifle sights again,' he added severely, and shot three bull's-eyes in succession, to Lenny's admiration and the manager's annoyance. 'And keep your cut-glass horrors, I'm not furnishing a morgue. Give the kid that golliwog,' said Mr Clark.

Hobson Clark was exactly the sort of man Lenny and her sisters had been warned against (never get into a car . . . accept sweets . . . come straight home and tell mother). He had a sports coat like a back-gammon board, and the shine on his patent leather pumps rivalled the shine on his blue-black hair. He wore a large ring and a larger tiepin and the sort of tie that Lenny had never even seen. Yet he didn't look wicked, but more like a character strayed from a story book.

'Anything else you fancy? Say the word,' Mr Clark invited. He won her a mauve vase and a kite and a tin alarm clock before she could say No Thank You.

There were swing boats outside, and bumper cars and a hoopla : they tried them all, shyly at first, then happily, then hilariously. Nobody swung higher or bumped harder or hooped more accurately than Hobson Clark. Lenny lost her hair ribbon, her panties showed and her shoelace broke. When they had tried everything they were breathless and laden with prizes, and Lenny had had five different kinds of ice-cream and cherry pop and candy floss and a sandwich.

'Excuse me, Mr Clark,' she said with great dignity, put down her prizes and was sick.

Hobson Clark was neither amused nor annoyed. He coped expertly, then steered her to a bright red sports car. 'This is really a taxi,' he told her. 'You'll have to give the driver your address.'

Lenny marched him straight into the drawing-room and introduced him to her mother, who was having a dress fitted by an aunt, and was immobilized with pins. Hobson Clark bowed and kissed her hand : he kissed the aunt's hand : he kissed Lenny's hand. He refused a cup of tea and left them gaping. But he was in and out of the house like a stormy petrel for the next ten years.

Hobson Clark was a publicity man (Lenny didn't understand what it was, at first) and he undertook any sort of publicity for an agreed fee—popularizing new furniture, or baby foods or débutantes or beauty queens or books that wouldn't sell or violinists who couldn't speak English or weddings or cream cheese. In between clients, he did a bit of his own, for he was a born exhibitionist. He risked life and limb and survived the most amazing situations unscathed. Some of his stunts, Lenny's family felt, were definitely not in good taste, but Hob was irrepressible and unsnubbable, and there was no doubting his kind heart. Did her father want to see an International when all seats at Twickenham were sold out : did her mother want a sewing machine or her sister a particular handbag : did her kid brother want an air-gun? Hob arrived with the article in his arms, eager as a terrier that's been down a particularly difficult rabbit hole. Margo and Daphne made use of him shamelessly, and even her parents were glad of his contacts. He knew everyone—generally to their discredit. He went everywhere —and came back again to Croydon. He was foolproof, fireproof, but not proof against Lenny.

He proposed to her on her seventeenth birthday, as she had known he would. He was curiously formal about it, and asked her father first. Lenny said No and burst into tears because, really, she did like him. In the end he had to lend her a handkerchief and mop her up

in time for her party. He proposed again on her eighteenth, nineteenth and twentieth birthdays, and Lenny managed to decline him more gracefully.

It was Hob put her on to modelling, of course. Told her how to set about it, contact the big fashion houses, which agencies to avoid, where to have her photographs taken. Lenny was grateful, because her family insisted on shorthand typing, and she really couldn't spell.

Between her nineteenth and twentieth birthdays, however, Hob made his big mistake. He introduced her to George : he was doing Waldo's publicity then. He repeated his proposal the night before her wedding, which upset her, because she saw he meant it.

'Hob, I'm marrying George. I love George.'

'You're marrying George and Waldo, my lovely.'

'Oh, Hob! You know you are—you'll always be—our best, our greatest friend.'

'Yes. Hobson's choice,' said Hob grimly.

Of course, it was true what he'd said, in a way. You said George and Waldo like you said Swan and Edgar, or Bacon and Eggs, or Stanley and Livingstone. They belonged together, indivisible, a unit. (Lenny had always been so confident that years hence, when there might not be a Waldo, George would be kept busy with the twins, or mowing the lawn, or even Good Works.)

It was a stunt of Hob's, of course, that really made Waldo a house-hold word. He found out the day before the Cup Final that the mascot of one of the teams had been run over. He rang up the bereaved team's manager (in the middle of the night) and suggested Waldo. The manager asked the captain. The captain asked his wife. His wife said, 'Anything you like, Ted, but put that light out before you wake the baby.' So Waldo was accepted.

Lenny rushed out and bought knitting wool in the team's colours. By lunch-time, she had a sleeveless pullover nearly ready. By kick-off time Waldo had arrived safely on the ground wearing it. The first team ran on to the ground and were cheered : Waldo's team ran on to the ground followed by Waldo, and hymns and popcorn and rattles were forgotten in the roar that followed. Several seats collapsed. Waldo, like a true showman, started playing to the crowd, and they loved it. Even George had difficulty getting him settled behind the home goal.

Of course, Waldo's team won, and it wasn't really a brilliant game, because every time one of the players looked at Waldo, he doubled up. So did the actress who kicked off, and the referee and police and ambulance men and a newsreel cameraman and three sporting bishops.

The winning captain, breathless and muddy, was handed up to the royal box to receive the cup, and Waldo of his own accord lumbered after him. How the crowd roared! Cameras clicked and newsreels whirred. There was the happy captain, clasping the cup (lopsided) and grinning, in the middle, and there were the Duke of Edinburgh and Waldo grinning at each other on either side. The picture was framed and pasted into scrapbooks and reproduced in colours and made into calendars and souvenir ashtrays for the rest of the year.

George was made—thanks to Hob and Waldo. He even left off wearing coloured monkey jackets and appeared with Waldo in tails and top hat. Lenny's family warmed to him considerably.

One night George announced that his old mother was ill down in Gloucestershire, and had sent for him. He took a very tender fare-well of Lenny (and Waldo) and set out for Paddington, particularly advising Lenny not to sit at home, waiting for him.

It was rather fun, being in the flat alone with Waldo. She groomed him as George had taught her, brushing, oiling and rubbing, which he adored. Meantime, she told him how much she loved George and how she missed him, even for a night : it took a long time. Waldo followed her from room to room, puffing slightly, till she turned on the radio for him. Waldo loved a good rowdy Variety programme.

He understood applause, and nothing pleased him better than rolling on his back and joining the studio audience in a hearty clap. After which he went to sleep behind the sofa. Lenny undressed for the night in her bedroom, came back and sat in front of the dying fire, brushing her hair and dreaming. It was very quiet.

It was after eleven when the doorbell rang. Hob, of course. But then Hob never seemed to eat or sleep or even work at normal hours. He laid a bunch of expensive white roses in her arms and Lenny pushed her empty cocoa cup under the nearest chair. 'Come and sit down,' she invited him, 'but not for long. I was just going to bed.'

'Where's George?' he asked. 'It seems quiet.'

'His mother's ill. He went down to Gloucestershire tonight,' Lenny said, unwillingly.

'Too bad, too bad,' murmured Hob. 'I bet he told you not to sit at home and wait!'

'Well . . .' Hob always knew what other people said and thought. It was uncanny of him. 'I was going to bed,' she repeated firmly.

'Slip a dress on and come out to a nightspot!'

'Certainly not. It's much too late.'

'It's never too late, my dear,' said Hob soberly. 'Any time you change your mind, Lenny, I'll be there.' He reached for her hand. 'But don't wait too long. We're wasting time, and even you are only young once.'

'No, Hob!' she disengaged her hand. Hob's great charm was that he was larger than life, much more highly coloured and not to be taken seriously.

'The first day I saw you, I knew I was going to love you. I'm not a monster, you know, to force my affections on a teenage girl. So I waited. I waited ten years. I don't mind about George: I like old George, but I think George is an incident in your life and that's all——'

'George is my husband,' retorted Lenny furiously.

'George and Waldo,' suggested Hob.

'And Waldo.' Lenny was in a corner. 'All right, Waldo too. But I'm happy.'

'You see, there is no George without Waldo, is there? Waldo made George, and I made Waldo! What's that thing they taught us as kids: Love is Service?'

It was unanswerable, but it was blackmail. Because he was there when my pants came down ten years ago in the High Street, and there when I hadn't a handkerchief in the school choir: because my sisters accepted so much, and I know Jack sponged on him, and even Daddy:

E

because he actually introduced George and me, and put Waldo on the map. . . .

'Oh, Hob!' Tears began to stream down her cheeks. 'Don't you see you were the big brother I never had, or the fairy uncle, and I'm grateful for all you've done for my family, and we're fond of you—George and I—I'm dreadfully fond of you, Hob. But I'd never leave George, never!'

'Well, at the moment, George seems to have left you!'

'But his mother's ill.'

'Did you see the telegram?'

'I don't have to,' said Lenny proudly.

'I see.' Hob tapped a cigarette on his case while Lenny wiped her face. 'He's often away, isn't he?'

'Really!' Lenny was exasperated. 'You know more about George's job than I do. Of course he goes away.' It was all very well to be on her dignity, but here she was in pink pyjamas and a blue housecoat and the clock on the mantelpiece said quarter to twelve. Thank goodness she hadn't started to cream her face. 'You're going home now,' she said decidedly. 'You know you're always welcome when George is here, but not tonight.' She held out his hat to him. 'Good night!'

'Lenny.'

'No.'

Oh, dear! Was he going to chase her all round her own drawing-room just because George was away? She had to ward him off with one hand and hold her housecoat together with the other. She jumped up and trod in the forgotten cocoa cup. 'Don't be silly!'

There was a movement behind the sofa. Roused by their voices, Waldo looked over the edge. His small eyes blinked. His Old Bill whiskers caught on the thick cloth as he moved his head from side to side like a charmed snake. He cleared his throat.

'Waldo?' called Lenny, relieved. She began to giggle. 'Look, we've woken him up!' Encouraged, Waldo came out and planted himself firmly between Hob and Lenny. Was this a game, a fight or a party?

Hob, defeated, kissed Lenny's hand above Waldo's enquiring head. 'Good night, my dear,' he said.

When he had gone, Lenny sat on the floor with an arm round Waldo, smiling into the dead fire. No girl was ever compromised who had two hundred and thirty pounds of performing sea lion for a chaperone.

In the next room, the phone began to ring. It was a trunk call from Gloucestershire.

An Anniversary

by *WALTER DE LA MARE*

Illustrated by Frederick Exell

A T least a minute—and one that resembled not only a sort of hole in Time but a pause in eternity—must have ticked its moments away; but even yet Aubrey could not be positively certain of what he had seen. Of the effect of just that one transfixed vague glimpse, his present attitude—long-chinned face thrust forward, cold, grey, light-lashed eyes peering fixedly through the budding tresses of his contorted weeping-ash—was evidence enough.

His earthenware pitcher still dangled from his numbed fingers. The blood in his throat and temples continued its faint drumming; the cause perhaps of a peculiar descending shimmer, as of motes of light, that now affected his vision. His eyes themselves, it seemed, had refused to let him make sure. He had been abjectly shaken—momentarily terrified even. The scalp on his head was still tingling. And yet he had continued to think.

He had made a habit of attending to what happened 'in his mind,' and was well aware that unpleasing memories, if they are steadily suppressed and driven down into the dark of that mind, may yet somehow grope their way up again and reappear in unexpected disguises.

Especially when one is not 'watching-out' for them! What then of this particular memory?

For a whole year it had stationed itself like a vague menacing shadow on the outskirts of consciousness. With anything so habitual one does not even have to look to see if it is still there ; just as in one's own house—at the end perhaps of a corridor, or on the landing of a stair-case, may hang a portrait which appears as if what it represented were always steadily in wait for—well, for a renewed and really close scrutiny of itself. And even though faces in portraits are only made of paint on canvas they can yet shed on one a sort of passive influence.

This inward shade that frequented Aubrey's mind was not how-ever a mere portrait. It was the vivid mental image of a 'friend' whom he had sufficient reason to distrust, and even detest, although its original must long ago, surely, have given up all earthly (or any other) concern with him. Or with Emily, either! The bourne from which, please God, no traveller returns. It had needed no Shakespeare to discover that! Why then quite unexpectedly—not out of the blue, perhaps—but out of these cold evening shadows? That was the ques-tion. A fantastic yet rather pressing question. What neglect there had been up to the present, had, it is true, been on one side only. The friend's. Not on Aubrey's. And he knew that he knew all that he needed to know of Emily.

When two minds, a man's and a woman's, are in close and frequent contact—or two bodies for that matter—each may, of course, be more or less aware even of what may be secretly passing in the other's. They seem to play eavesdropper too, not only to each other's thoughts but even to each other's sensations. But then, women are assumed to be more sentimental than men. More sentimental at any rate than Aubrey was himself by nature, or than he had any intention of being. Over anniversaries, for example—birthdays, red-letter days, promise-days, love-days, death-days. It was fantastic. It was as if their hearts were their calendars—dismally trustworthy calendars in the clearest of print. To let the dead past bury not only its dead but also its moribund, and bury it deep, had always been—by much—Aubrey's private preference.

On the other hand jealousy is a sinister evil. It conduces to an increasing, active and wearisome hatred. Hack away as you will at its roots and suckers they will begin sprouting again even in the small hours of a single night. They become entangled with the instincts and are the hops and bramble and bindweed of the imagination. Trailing, tender, almond-scented bindweed—Aubrey had read somewhere—will

penetrate even into loamy churchyard sod and soil a sheer nine feet. 'Full fathom five.' But that *he* should ever have fallen a prey to jealousy! And with nothing but envy and a worn-out passion, no affection even, for its justification!

Apart from any reasons, however—and hatred no more than love positively needs any—he had at first sight taken a sudden hatred to John Fiske. In the whole wide world he was certain there was nothing they could have agreed about. 'Oil and vinegar,' yes ; but there had been no salad. One can sneer at, despise, and label an enemy stolid, and yet realize that it would be nearer the mark if in the last epithet one omitted the 't.' In spite of his cursed 'honesty,' his stubborn directness and stupider devotion (to what did not belong to him), John Fiske had been as hard to see through as he had been to explore. More impenetrable indeed even than the gloom now steadily deepening beneath the branches of this weeping-ash.

Besides, Aubrey had been envious of Fiske long before he had become jealous of him. Not because he thought him as quick and clever —and certainly not as attractive—as himself. It was his dull, suety, stupid good qualities that he abominated most. They can be the very devil when one wants the owner of them out of the way. As for his own good qualities—brains, morals, heart? He'd have given himself a *plus* for the first. And the rest? Well, according to taste! Also he knew what he wanted. As, of course, in his slow, honest-to-god, idiotic fashion had Fiske. Precisely how much of his own particular *want* had he got? By no means all ; Aubrey himself had seen to that. And yet . . . to hell with him!

There, indeed, so far as undertaker, sexton, and the passing of time can manage, was precisely where he might perhaps be ; and for good! Though, somehow, the clever seems to be its likelier inhabitants. Why on earth then was he himself dithering about like this, outside this arboreal cage, and extremely reluctant to venture into it? Solely because it had for that split second seemed to be *occupied* : and by a vigilant and tongueless intruder loafing in wait by a damp-greened old water-butt—his clock a dripping tap!

Aubrey's first symptoms of shock having now subsided, one simple question presented itself. Since what he had seen, or had appeared to see, could by no possibility be actual—not at any rate as actual as the water-butt—could it have been 'real'? If real, it would prove a deadly nuisance, and might entail the vilest complications. If not real, it had been merely an illusion.

'Ghosts'—pah! No, from that bourne *no* traveller returns ; and that may be damned bad luck for those beyond it! Dead men rise up never ; no matter into what Dead Sea even the weariest river may eventually wind its way. Apart from their bones and their worldly goods the only thing the dead leave behind them is their memory. But that—such is the imbecility of the human mind—however secretly it is hidden, may, as Emily would agree, become an obsession. And obsessions may breed illusions. With them, bell, book and candle are of far less service than *pot. brom.* A sneer webbed over Aubrey's cold stiff features. For, with Emily, even *pot. brom.*, let alone her Evening Services, tame-cattiness and deadly taciturnity, had failed.

Real or not, it was just like Fiske to have chosen this particular place and time for—well, this reunion. During the lingering days of autumn how often at his work in the City used Aubrey's fascinated fancy to turn to this last half-hour of twilight in his long straggling garden : these motionless, misty, earthy, early October evenings, the last of the sunset dying in the west. He loved the reek of his leaf bonfires and the almost nutty odour of decay. He loved being alone ; or, rather perhaps, being in strict privacy. And here, even at noonday, his garden was screened from the direct scrutiny of his neighbours. He was a person who refused not only to allow himself to be neglected, but to be overlooked. There are eyes indeed that, once met, cannot even in memory be overlooked.

Apart from direct access by way of the house, the only route into and out of Aubrey's garden lay by a wicket-gate that led into the open —into wide, flat and now fog-bound fields of damp and malodorous cabbages and cauliflowers, sour acres and acres of deserted market gardens. Back from his day in London, he delighted in pottering and, hardly less, in pretending to potter. A perpetual and pleasing activity of mind usually accompanied this busy do-little. He was abnormally secretive. For weeks he had held his tongue while that little romance of 'yesteryear' had steadily intensified and his own particular little intentions and designs had no less steadily matured. And even this no doubt was in part because of his peculiar pleasure in his own society ; even at its worst. He positively enjoyed a festering stagnant mood. Not that many human beings are not pleasanter when they are alone. It is an eventuality that may be of equal advantage to their friends.

Indeed, who would deny that it is chiefly the presence of one's fellow-creatures that evokes one's worst though these may possibly be one's rarest, characteristics! Alone, even by no means virtuous people may mean wholly well. Not so Aubrey. He despised what he called cant, and first and foremost he *meant* business. It was, too, in the solitude of his garden, particularly as dusk thickened, that he could best explore his little plans. Then, as if with a dark lantern, he could follow up the wavering, intersecting paths leading into the future. Digging, hoeing, and even weeding, helped him to concentrate. He was something of a sapper, too ; sly and sedulous when things or people stood in his way.

He was a thirsty creature too ; delighted in cold water especially, and drank large quantities of it. For one thing, it was all but free. It was, then, a special pleasure—his gardening done for the day—to sally off down to the water-butt under this weeping-ash, and there fill his earthenware pitcher. For himself, and for the flowers indoors. It was due, perhaps, to the Old Adam in him, after the fall of Eve. Also he had a nice taste in flowers. One might almost describe him as an intellectual aesthete who, coming into this unrighteous world, had been deprived of a start.

At this very moment, as he stood listening, he could hear from under the tree the furtive falling sing-song of the waterdrops out of the pump's iron spout—a tuneless tune, either entirely heedless of its surroundings, or, contrariwise, endeavouring to warn him of something amiss. But what? Just lately, as the days drew in, it had been more than dusk, it had been all but dark, when he had abandoned his flower-beds. The first stars would be pricking into the sky. He would stand, looking up ; amused to remind himself that these sparkling darlings of the poets and sentimentalists are nothing but remote and unimaginably immense vats of gas or 'energy'—anything you please, except the pretty-pretty. That, beyond inconceivably icy Saharas of pitch-black space, they are not only at some appalling velocity hastening towards (or was it way from) man's silly little solar system, but are also running *down* ! It was an anarchistic little notion that made him laugh. *All* of us, every one of us, doomed! What concern had they indeed with human affairs?—celestial glow-worms, devoid even of harbouring a consciousness! His *own* 'star' was quite another matter. That was *his* concern ; or, at any rate, he meant to make it so.

And now, large as life, as reserved, as unfathomable, and—damn his eyes—as coldly contemptuous of Aubrey himself as ever, here was this devil, Fiske, or his double, or his revenant, his astral body or mere presentment, masquerading in the shelter of Aubrey's very own private weeping-ash !

'Come back,' had he! What for? *Whom* for? Ah, yes! In that maze we call the mind, (and heart too), even an illusion may have a purpose and a motive, though either may remain securely hidden in the unconscious. If this was solely his own illusion and he himself was its only goal, well and good. But suppose Emily . . .? No, he badly needed that there should be no meddling with her. Not yet, anyhow. And to confess to an illusion! *To her!* Not on your life!

The fact was, he was being compelled to pay attention to a mere trick of his senses, to a silly hallucination—which might none the less tend to become a repeated hallucination. With the advent of this new notion Aubrey suddenly changed his mind. A bright idea! Why *not* presently make mocking mention to Emily of this little adventure —and watch *her* reactions. It would all sound so probable, and so natural, and so harmless.—'Yes, darling, just now. As a matter of fact—having finished up—I was just going to fill the water-pot when . . .' There had been too much futile reserve and conceal- ment during these last months : the first vindictive indictments and persecutions over : before the stagnancy had set in. Far better perhaps bring the whole stupid business into the open again. Yes, and keep it there. If his fancies intended to prey on him, they might in that case not have to prey for very long. Every female heart has its snapping-point. The elastic perishes.

What need then was there to worry? Solely and solidly, of course, because all this entailed a little question of £ s. d. 'Ghosts,' whatever their texture, may gibber ; but *money* talks. And loudly, too, if one has the need or the desire to listen. Had Emily, or had she not, made another will? If she had, then he could be practically certain of disaster. And for the life of him he could not conceive of any hiding- place as yet unattended to. Not at least in the house. If she had not : well, better not inquire too closely. In any case she had not for- gotten.

That covertly scrutinized tell-tale face! The lurking shadows, the hauntedness beneath those rounded eyelids, had never left it. Neither by day nor by night had it lost either its pallor or its settled melancholy. An abandoned Ophelia, suckling a secret so intense and so profound. Those long lapses too into silence and vacancy. Recently he had done his level best to let that particular sleeping dog lie. And in so doing how much he had missed the amusing but now forbidden sport of stirring its maudlin slumbers. Passive resistance, passive accep- tance—which was the most galling? He had begun to fancy, too, that slander—or intuition—had been busy with his own little activities.

Supposing, then, that, after all, with her pestilent mother for accom- plice, she was debating, still in doubt, whether or not to leave him? No guile, no subtlety, not even his own, could extort so much as a nod from her on that. Was she herself less candid, less transparent than he had supposed? Well, she had discovered long ago what kind of fish she had netted ; or been netted by. Why, then, was he fudging and faltering like this?

There had been a light rain that evening, gently weeping clouds ; and only at this moment had he become aware that a newish moon was sinking in the west—a moon well on her way to her first quarter, faintly silvering the ash twigs, vaguely curdling the gloom within. How easily might his recent little experience have been a pure deceit? And yet, could the mere misconception of some familiar object have continued active for so long? How many moments—minutes—had he been caught up in this idiotic trance?

Aubrey stooped a little, shut his eyes very tight for a few instants, then opened them again. Idiot! The effort had only made them less effective. Those scintillant luminous motes poured softly on.

At length, lifting his left hand—as gently as a Gehazi peering in upon an Elisha—he drew a fan of twigs an inch or two aside.

'Well!' he heard his dry lips calling softly into the gloom. 'What about it, then? . . . Is that you, Fiske?'

*   *   *   *   *

In the complete history of mankind never surely had a more imbecile question been addressed into a silence so intent. Not a single syllable of this dramatic little adjuration had been consciously present in his mind until he had heard his own voice utter it. A queer voice too. And no wonder. There, in every obscure detail, utterly motionless, mutely and tranquilly challenging, the illusion had taken shape again —or in the interval had remained unaffected. There was no active speculation in those eyes—nor assuredly anything approaching a 'glare.' They were still faintly luminous and serenely inquiring, as if in some remote meditation. At this overwhelming proof of his beastly predicament, provoked too perhaps by the shaken and muffled tones of his own voice, and the effort to stop his teeth chattering, Aubrey's wits had become slightly unbalanced. He stooped lower ; coughed : he was afraid.

'Whoever you are, *what*ever you are,' he heard his swollen tongue declare, 'you have no bloody business to be here. Understand that! You—! If you want me—or anybody else, for that matter—you know where the gate is, and you can go round to the front. Do you hear me? Go round to the front, curse you ; and knock like a gentleman!'

But had he in fact uttered these words? Or had he only overheard one of those inward interlopers who begin so garrulously shouting into one's ear on the very brink of sleep? He had, at any rate, *thought* them ; and the rebuke had done something to restore his confidence. He knew—oh, absolutely—that no answer would come. He defied an answer. Indeed, the only perceptible change in his surroundings— the faintest of changes—was that the deepening darkness into which he was peering had been very feebly diminished. As cautiously as an animal venomously resentful of its cage he glanced over his shoulder. Well, he had bidden his visitor go round to the front and knock ; and knock like a gentleman. And now, as if for a symbol of how warmly he would be welcomed, a light, which must momentarily have shone out and down from an upper window of the house behind him, had suddenly gone out. Its walls and windows were blank again as a sepulchre's.

This time, too, when he himself wheeled swiftly round again, there was absolutely nothing to be seen but his very own familiar pump beneath its writhen wattled tent of intertwining ash-boughs. And a silence had fallen, curdled only by one tiny monotonous watery whimper, intent not only on repeating the same tune on and on and over and over again, but on *singing* it! God help him! Counterfeit or not, the 'Black Man' had certainly taken shape. The shape of Fiske.

And, although Aubrey's lean, long-chinned face, his pale eyes and brass-coloured hair hardly suggested that he was likely to be the victim of nerves, this precisely was what he was 'up against' now. . . . And for how long? He swallowed the hoarse laugh of bravado that had slid into his throat before it had become audible, and for yet another moment or two still hesitated to intrude, from out of the open, into the little tent of darkness that until this evening had been his all but unfailingly happy heritage as tenant of his garden. What the eye cannot see, the skin may become aware of! Still, go right in he did at last, and waited until his pitcher was three parts full, striving the while to breathe less quickly the dank autumnal air, and to slow up his silly heartbeats. He was alone now, acutely so. His visitor, his visitant, had absconded. But never never again would his idolized garden be able to convince him that his solitude was absolute and complete.

The mists from the rain-soaked flats beyond his wicket-gate were now not only visible but smellable and tasteable. Whereas his late visitant—well, he could not say what precise conspiracy of his senses had been responsible for *him*. He had certainly not been audible.

'So much for that!' Aubrey muttered to himself, as he gave a violent wrench to the tap in the hope of silencing its silly, officious, doll-like musical box. 'Now for the rest of the play!' He even regretted he had not reminded his meddlesome enemy that there was a notice-board at the gate out of the market-gardens proclaiming :—'No Admittance except on Business.'

*   *   *   *   *

The faint tinkle of a bell sounded from the house behind him. He swore under his breath. 'That's just what these idiots *would* be doing at such a moment.' And as yet he had had no time for a wash or to change his gardening boots—clumpers, half-an-inch thick with sodden soil. He took out his handkerchief and wiped his face and head. He was exhausted, solely by the strain of standing motionless, for, perhaps, three complete minutes! Or was it months? He must go back ; and quickly. A cold, jagged smile broke over his features. Supposing, that little while ago, he had been taken at his word! A rat-tat-tat-tat? . . . *Qui vive?* . . . Who knows?

Or had what had happened in the solitude of the garden been only a novel and beastly symptom of one of his own familiar little attacks? Yet another bout—and as early as October! A glimpse of himself, feeble and sweating on a sick-bed, swam into his view. How much he loathed the repeated parrot-like inquiries, and that evening tray laden with its tail-swallowed whiting, or insipid minced chicken, and miniature 'light pudding.' Or tapioca! That would be when he was getting better. Getting better, yes : but then, you never knew!

However, he was no weakling. He had schooled himself in the past to face what comes, and particularly if he had arranged for it. Dunning letters, for example ; plea-ful letters ; indiscreet, passionate, aggrieved outpourings of the heart ; rate-collectors ; and now and then the moneylender's jackal. Just wait! And above all, keep calm! Think before you speak. Watch! And never never—unless you are positively cornered—never lose your temper or your balance.

Unless, in the next world, space is of no consequence, unless time is non-existent in eternity, it would take his revenant, his spook, if not his hallucination, at least ten minutes to get round from his garden gate to the front door. Why, he wondered, must the thought of a slow but sure walking apparition be so much less savoury in the fancy, than, say, the classic method devised for its reappearance by the usual medium? A Fiske consisting of ectoplasm! And why was he himself *still* listening? The squeal of his front gate could be heard a mile off. But had he shut it? What the hell was the use of asking himself such fatuous questions?

He pushed back his handkerchief into his pocket, lifted his pitcher of well-water—twice as heavy as it had ever been before—trod steadily and stealthily back to the house, set it down on the stones in the back porch, opened the door and went in.

The fusty room beyond, although it contained his pet primulas and gloxinias, was scarcely worthy of being called a conservatory, and there was only darkness now to see his treasures by ; so that, when he opened the french window and pushed back the curtain that concealed the dining-room beyond, the instantaneous electric blaze for the instant all but blinded him. It was as sudden as a blow in the face.

The room was vacant ; but everything lay ready on the table and on the sideboard, flowers, china, silver, shining and twinkling there, mute and peaceful. 'Still life!' He glanced at the clock on the chimneypiece—a wedding-present. It began to tick. He went softly in, then out into the demure, scrupulously clean and garnished little 'hall' beyond. Fingers and thumb on the newel of its post, he paused at the foot of the staircase.

And, as if he had been heard listening—'Oh ; is that you, Aubrey? Supper's ready,' a voice called faintly from upstairs. 'I am just coming. I was getting a handkerchief.'

'Right, darling!' he shouted back, but louder than he had intended. 'But don't come down. I am coming up. I must have a wash. I was kept in the garden. I mean I could not get . . .'

' "Kept in the garden" '? echoed the voice, a little nearer now, and even as if the owner of it were awaiting, even dreading, what so simple an explanation might mean, although he had carefully refrained from making unusual by even a fraction of a tone a single syllable of it.

'Don't come down,' he repeated. 'I am coming up—this moment.' He paused to swallow. 'Everything all right?' Dam' fool!

'Oh, very well,' came the answer, yet faintlier. 'Yes, everything. I shall be in the bathroom. I am getting a hot-water bottle.'

A hot-water bottle! The old self-pampering. Mere invalidism—and doctor's bills. The old 'pains,' he supposed. But surely she couldn't be going to bed! 'Clay—clay-cold is my earthy mouth.' . . . How *did* the old borderland jingle go?

Treading with an almost cat-like punctilio on the mats from door to door, with two almost soundless intervening steps on the linoleum between them, he made his way into the kitchen. All that for the moment he could see of its only inmate was a hummock of black skirts, a strip of what appeared to be a petticoat, and exposed heels. The rest of her was concealed by the open door of the gas oven.

'Mary,' he cried softly. 'Don't dish up just yet. I am not ready. And—'

A long, dark and intent face had made its appearance above the oven-door.

'What I was going to say,' he explained, 'is that—well, there *may* be a visitor. And I don't want Mrs Silcot to be worried just now. She seems to be overtired.'

Yet again he listened to an ejected statement that he could have taken his Bible oath he had never meant to make. Well, he must stick to it.

The dark stare from above the oven-door had intensified. Sullen rat! Who paid her wages?

'A visitor! . . . Staying for supper!'

'Yes. Oh, no. I didn't mean that. Only that if anyone should knock whom you may not recognize—don't *necessarily* ask him in. I see there is no light in the hall yet; I'll switch that on first. It may, of course, be nothing at all; merely a false alarm. I mean, of course, there's only a possibility . . . In the City this afternoon . . .'

Why had the stolid colourless face stirred not so much as an eyelid? Merely stared?

'I mean,' he fumbled on, 'if no one comes, it does not matter. Obviously. There is no need to wait about, I mean; except not to dish up for the moment. But, if so—*if* anyone should—then just come to *me*, and say, "A Mr Hamilton wishes to see you. It's about a picture." Something of that kind. I am not suggesting, mind—' and an all but winsome smile edged into his grey features—'that it *will* be a Mr Hamilton. Or about a picture. It might be somebody else. However, that will be all right. *I* shall understand. Do you see what I mean?'

Mary abruptly turned her head away; paused, as it seemed, to exchange a few words with the interior of the oven; then rose to her feet. She then firmly shut-to the oven-door. She knew that she had been watching him more intently than was necessary while he had given his directions, his 'orders.' But then you can never be sure what some people are up to. *That* rigmarole!—and a face like a half-starved ferret. She looked at him again pointblank, with her pitch-black, disciplined eyes. A bleak, plain, honest stare; and intelligent.

'Very good, sir,' she said. 'You don't know whether or not. But *if* so, a Mr Hamilton. I quite understand. But nobody extra. And whoever it is, I am to say, "a Mr Hamilton" . . . Mrs Silcot is poorly again?'

'Ah,' Aubrey answered the tone of her remark, not its meaning. 'Yes, I am sorry.'

Yet again his rasp-edged temper had nearly got the better of him. Of what consequence was it what a servant thought or felt? No *love* was lost between them! Let her do as she was told, or get out. Even Emily would agree to that. Or would she? Even the dustman was a devotee of Emily's. As quietly as if he were a strange cat in his own house he turned away from the kitchen and its hated inmate and mounted the stairs. Arrived at the bathroom, he paused at the open door, watching for a while Emily bathed in the bright electric light within, as she stood, head thrown back, gargling over the basin.

'What's wrong now?' he inquired.

'Oh,' said Emily, ejecting the mouthwash. 'It's this geyser. It takes such an age to heat up. I thought I would have my bath a little earlier.'

'That, darling, is because you never manage it right,' he retorted. 'And anyhow it's better than getting the water scalding hot out of the tap before you can say knife. What I really meant was, what's the matter with *you*?'

'Matter?' she echoed, glancing apprehensively over her shoulder. 'I didn't say anything was the matter, Aubrey. Only I think I shall have to go to bed soon after dinner. The same old thing.'

'As I supposed,' said Aubrey. And now her too-large luminous eyes had also suddenly become fixed on his fair pallid features. An ingenuous but searching scrutiny had met a viper-like stare in an instantaneous conflict of questioning.

'What was it you called up about the garden just now? You look as white as a ghost. You're not ill, Aubrey?'

The mask had all but taken to itself the appearance of plaster of paris. It had set so hard.

'That's merely your way of getting even ; of evasion, my dear. An old dodge, that,' he answered as sweetly as his mouth would let him. 'I stumbled—fetching water in the garden. And anyhow, what are we waiting for? *Mary* ? There is never—I say, *never*—a single meal in this house on the tick. And surely you aren't going to suggest that that has anything to do with the geyser?'

Emily paused a moment in the act of stooping to put down the

kettle, and was now screwing in the stopper of the water-bottle. She watched her fingers.

'The bell rang about five minutes ago,' she said.

'Look here, Emily,' Aubrey broke out, 'it's not a particle of use your attempting to come down to supper. You just sham that these aches and pains are of no importance, and so only make them worse. You are to go to bed *now* ; and the janitrix shall bring you up something on a tray—some nice minced chicken, and a cup of cocoa, perhaps.' He had listened to this idiotic irony, and his stomach had fallen. 'Keep friends!' urged an inward voice.

Emily paused a second time. She had gradually fallen into the habit, during these last months, of thinking over every answer she was on the point of making to her husband, before its terms became irretrievable.

'I am very sorry,' she said at last. 'But isn't that a little inconsistent? There can't be anything seriously "wrong." At least. . . . Of course there can't. And you have always said that it's best not to pay attention to such things. You have always said, "Wait for them to make you do so." There was only a little faintness. And—well, just here.' But her left hand was already stationed over her breast-bone.

Almost as if an hour-glass hung suspended in the air before his eyes, Aubrey was watching the sands of time as they soundlessly glided away.

'First it was aches and pains,' he argued. 'Now it is "a little faintness." ' These women!

'And wasn't it *I*—' he had raised his voice a little—'wasn't it *I* who at last insisted on your seeing the doctor again? And wasn't it *I* who insisted on his sounding and ninety-nining you and flourishing that absurd rubber contraption in his ladylike fingers—careless devil? And didn't he *say* that he could find nothing organically wrong? Pah! " Organically!" Good heavens, I had a heart for years—when I was a boy ; and was not even taken off football. All that palaver! This vague haze of suggestion. " Symptoms!" They invent complications ; phobias, as *they* call them. It pays.'

Emily had turned away, pretending still to be drying the dumb rubber mouth of her hot-water bottle with a towel. By biting her lips perhaps she could better keep her mouth shut.

'Of course . . . I'll go at once. But honestly, there is no need.'

Aubrey drew back—a little too much for it to have been instinctive —behind the door, as she closely passed him by.

'I never even uttered the word "need," he called after her, and then

F

on second thoughts followed her into her bedroom, pausing only a moment to dip his head over the rail of the landing, though he failed to catch a glimpse of the front door.

'*Ouff*,' he grumbled. 'One could dine off merely the smell of the cooking in this house before tasting a mouthful. *That* fool!'

Emily was already drawing the short curtains over the windows. He watched her face intently as she turned down the sheet of her bed. So slow and laborious was every movement that it might have been a sheet of lead. And at every turn, when she hoped she was unobserved, she glanced back at him. What was really wrong? she was meditating. What was behind all this? When a man is tired and hungry one has to hold one's tongue. Anyhow, it's best to, however unfair and morose he may be. Yes, hold it like a tactful, vigilant child—the child, thank God, they were never going to have. And this time, like a wicked child, *he* was complaining not because there was anything to complain of, but because there was not.

She folded the bedspread, lifted the bedclothes, and pushed in the bottle between the sheets.

'There, now,' she said, gingerly smiling round at him, 'that's all. But you know, Aubrey, how I hate going to bed. Please don't let there be much on the tray.' She suppressed a faint shudder. 'I am not really hungry.'

He hesitated. How the devil was he ever to get to the point? Somewhere in the far dark of his mind he heard approaching footsteps, faint as the coming of feet on wool, like a man weightless as a shadow walking in snow. Snow!

'The fact is, Emily, what is really worrying and fretting you is the conviction that you ought to see a specialist. Then why—whatever apart from fees and humbug that blessed word implies, and it means of course having that wretched doctor back again—why don't you *say* so? I wish to God we had someone we could depend on in this miserable neighbourhood.' He paused again, watching her. 'What, Emily, by the way, was the name of that fellow at Ambrey? A tall man, stiff as a board ; with a nose and spectacles? *He* seemed to know his business.'

Emily had sat down. She was stooping as if to draw off her shoe, and at this she fixed her eyes as intently on it as if the thing could speak.

'You mean Dr McLechlan?'

'Yes, Dr McLechlan. That's it. Dr Mucklechchlan. Just like that! The snuffy Scotchman. You wouldn't, I suppose, like to see *him*?'

'But surely—' she paused. 'Don't you remember? He sold his practice nearly a year ago and went—wasn't it?—to Canada.'

'Was it?' Aubrey continued to stare at his face in the looking-glass. Better, better, better to get down to brass tacks ; to have it out. Just in case. And other things too. The dead past cannot always take care of itself—with the future in view.

'Canada, eh? That's a long way off. You have a remarkable memory for dates, Emily. You never, never forget. And yet, after all, it would be no great loss : not now. He may have been clever ; but he was a trifle underhanded, don't you think? Even fishy? But *his* friend? Don't you remember on the river that awful day in August when we sat in the boat under a bridge while the rusty rain dripped on and on into the salad? That seems a devil of a time ago. What was *his* name?'

She hadn't stirred. So that was it?—at last. Again! Not all omens prove false. 'You *know* his name, Aubrey. You are only pretending. . . . You are stirring up. . . . Why?'

Aubrey watched himself laugh in the glass ; though silent laughter more closely resembles a grimace. 'Of course,' he drawled, 'I know his name. The "Reverend" John Fiske. He *ought* of course to have gone into the Church. You agree to that? He might have some day become an archdeacon : gaiters and laced-up chapeau. In spite of the buns and oranges, it needs strong, silent men. Another anniversary, Emily. You had a very soft spot in that rebellious, susceptible heart of yours for him. Once. It was quite a dare.'

Emily had at last managed to take off the second shoe, and had reached, with a shuddering sigh, for her bedroom slippers. Well, she must go on, she supposed. 'Your dinner won't be improving,' she said.

'But . . . but what is the use, what is the purpose,' she went on, 'of pretence? Oh, heavens, haven't we had that all out again and again ; ages, ages ago? You were talking of doctors. Dr McLechlan was an excellent doctor.'

'So it's to be "All change"—for the time being?' Aubrey inquired sarcastically. 'I didn't say he was not a good doctor. I didn't even say he was not an excellent doctor. But were you quite satisfied— afterwards? I have often wondered ; though I don't remember to have mentioned it. But perhaps you hadn't much opportunity for thinking. Too far gone ; stricken.'

'I refuse to ask or answer any more questions, Aubrey. Why, I mean, you have brought all this up again now. I should not have supposed that just mocking at anyone at . . . yes, at a loss like that, was . . . But what I *am* asking now is, did you really have any doubt about Dr McLechlan?'

'Well, you see, I happened to know Dr McLechlan myself person-ally, and he talked the case over with me.   Mockery, a quite natural little grievance and all that aside, I never *wanted* to dig it all up again. But if you must know, he told me himself that he had not really been satisfied.   Regarding the result of his treatment of the case, I mean. And that *then* it was too late.'

'Too late?'

'Yes, too late.   And I, well, really, I didn't care a dam'.   Though, as a matter of fact, I was not so sure myself that I agreed with him.'

' " Agreed "?'

'My dear Emily, I do wish you would make a little effort to get over the habit of just repeating every word one says.   It's call cuckoo-ing. It gains time, of course.   I say, I didn't agree with him that it *was* too late.'

'Then, did you tell him so?   Did you?   I want to know that.'   She bent still lower over her knees.

'*I*—tell him?' said her husband.   'Certainly not.   It is not for a mere layman to butt in—though that's what they lie in wait for.   "Tell me what's the matter with you, then I'll tell *you*!"   That's their tack.'

'You mean,' she said, rising with a sigh of difficulty to her feet and facing him in the full light of the lamp over the dressing-table, scattered over with its shining glass, cosmetics and *gewgaws,* 'you mean, *you* let it go?   That it need not have been fatal—that he himself. . . . Oh, oh, I wish I were dead!'   She flung her hands apart, and gazed steadily back at him.   'But why do you ask *me*?'

'*Me*?' echoed he, in quiet derision.   'Oh, I like that, and which "he" may I ask?   Why do I ask *her* about *him*?   That's pretty good.   I was right, however, about the soft spot.   And, oh yes, I agree that we have discussed all this, or nearly all this before—and the precise quality of the softness.   Nor, Emily, are you by any means the only person in this world who has ever wished to be dead.   And in "a better world," as they call it.   But even from any kind of world some of us may now and then come back out again—alive-like, if not positively kicking. From "the other side," I mean.   Even on this.   A very few.   What I am really wanting to know, though—and please do try to be reason-able and calm about it—what I soberly and truly am pining to know is what would you do if—say, tomorrow evening—I happened to meet our friend (*not* Dr McLechlan), and asked him home to supper with us?'

'After what you have said, Aubrey, and you don't seem to see, or even to suspect how awful it is about knowing and not saying whether or not Dr McLechlan even suggested that he—that he need not have died. . . . No, I refuse to say anything more.'

" 'She takes refuge in silence," ' Aubrey silently protested to the All-Highest. 'And *that*,' he added, 'is just where, my dear, you are at last on the right tack. . . . So your precious Dr McLechlan went off to Canada, did he? And if there was anything out of the common, a little mysterious ; well, we can't ask him now, can we? No address. . . . In either case——'

'And I say to that,' said Emily, 'that not one of John's friends ever said a word that even suggested that. Anything "mysterious," I mean.'

'For heaven's sake don't keep niggling,' said her husband. 'It's just like a pretty pollie parrot. You will agree, you can't help agreeing, that you only had Dr McLechlan's word for it. Actually. That his patient had just finally retired, I mean. We omitted attending the funeral, didn't we? You said I somehow *made* you lose the train. Charitable. Besides, after all this time, why on earth should you mind so simple a question? Merely, if I *had* happened to meet the afflicted one this afternoon? Well, then, good God, he couldn't be dead, could he? Though it might suggest that he was a bit restless? On the other hand, does even an "excellent" doctor never make mistakes? And especially if he wishes to do not one forlorn friend, but two, a little favour. You'll agree that that's an ingenious little suggestion. Even though I was gracious enough to accept him at his word. There is always that horrid little inquisition about one's having been in one's right mind. Still, a lie is a lie, even if there are grey and commendable ones as well as white. And just a word—a word that would finally put our friend John out of any needlessly unhappy thoughts concerning him, would certainly have been kind, and perhaps even condonable. For both your sakes.'

Aubrey had ventured further into his own fantastic, pitiless trap than he had intended. His mouth remained ajar, in spite of his intention to shut it ; and yet again he found himself listening, though his eyes, reflected in the quicksilver of the glass, continued to watch, as Emily came near. She even persuaded herself to lay a hand on his sleeve, to touch him.

'You are torturing me. You are beginning again, even if—even if it should be for the last time. It was Dr McLechlan himself who told me that you went to see him. That you even sat with John that afternoon the day before the night he—he died. Listen,' her eyes were scrutinizing his face as though in search of what until this moment she could never so much as imagine could be discoverable there—discoverable even there. 'Listen!' she repeated, 'you *know* that you are hinting at what is absolutely untrue. You know that Dr McLechlan did his very best and . . . Oh, I can't bear it. What has happened? Something has *happened*, I say. Unless you want to—well, to finish me off, you must tell me. You will have to tell me.'

'Oh-ho,' Aubrey scarcely more than muttered the words, breathing heavily through distended nostrils, 'so now we are coming down to the naked facts! Not very pleasant, either. So you couldn't bear that little taradiddle, even now. Not even the mere hypothesis. Strange, though, it never even occurred to you. Wouldn't it have clinched the— the . . . ? But there, Emily, husbands after all will be husbands. You must have realized that long ago. And Fiskes will be Fiskes. "Fiskes!"—doesn't that sound just awful? What kind of an animal, do you think, would a Fiske resemble? No. No. I am *not* questioning the death certificate. I was merely, well, making up. But just to clear things up a little further, more tidily, let me put it in another way. Not, mind you, that mistakes have never been made. Sleeping draughts —that kind of thing. Even wrong identifications—that kind of thing. Bricks instead of bodies. The shockers are full of them. Why, there was a play produced, only about a month ago, on that very subject. But, there, let's drop all that. Supposing, Emily, *not* what I said just now. But just supposing that *he* appeared—*appeared* to have come back, I mean? This Fiske of ours? What then? Not him*self*, of course, you know, but. . . . You—you *liked* him?'

Emily had drawn back, and had huddled, rather than seated herself, at the foot of the bed, her hands, like a bird's claws, clutching its edge.

'I see,' she replied, though her face at the moment revealing nothing but the mingled glooms and darknesses of doubt and horror. 'I *see* You were only persecuting me. You were putting these vile and awful things into my mind, first, merely to watch their effect, and then—and with such gentle fingers!—and then to see the effect of taking them out again. And yet' (she added the words almost pensively, as if a voice had whispered a little secret to her which there was now no immediate need either to explore or to ponder over), 'and yet, the cruel memory of them remains to fester. No poor wretch, I suppose, forgets his torturers because they restored him to consciousness : only in order to begin again. Very well, then. Let us be quite, quite clear, and for the last time. . . .

'You ask me if I *liked* him. That question, and you know it, and though I detest saying it, came only out of the old malice and—and cynicism. *"Liked"* him? I liked him beyond words to tell! As one likes—well, being one's self and being happy. As one likes what has remained true and familiar and of one's very self ever since childhood. Also, I loved him. He was the all that I had never even dreamed of. Yes, have it all out now! There will be no other chance. And I was *in* love with him. Everything that that can imply, body, heart and mind. And you know that, too. And yet. . . . No ; you will never, never be able to grasp the true meaning of anything so simple. Not a vestige of that is in your nature. Never. Not at any rate until you break yourself on your own miserable rack. And now, because you had the best of it—and what a best!—you think you can go on and on having the best of me. Taunting me, mocking me, torturing me. Lying and laughing in my face. Who would have believed such lies were even thinkable. Well, now I have owned it. And you can persecute me no more.'

'No? "Quoth the Raven, *Nevermore!*" ' A peculiar leer spread over his sallow face. 'Ashamed of it?'

' "Ashamed!" ' What is there to be ashamed of? What *was* there to be ashamed of? Had you *never* been, never even supposed yourself to be in love? Not even as a child? Before you had the misfortune to meet *me*?'

'Oh, very, very funny!' cried Aubrey, his face wreathed in grimaces, 'Misfortune! Misfortune!'—he barked it out so loud in the room that a thin glass ornament on the dressing-table fairly tinkled with amusement. 'But, see here, my pretty romantic bird, what I am saying is— not so much that you *were* in love with the departed gentleman, who, having failed in securing his dot-and-carry-one, *may* have passively accepted his wretched failure and indulged in a sort of go-slow strike against life—but that you still are! Answer me that! And if, living or dead, he came back now. . . . Well, are you? Answer me *that*!'

The rasp of his half-suffocated voice seemed to corrode the air. And it appeared as if every contour, every line and edge of her face had altered as he looked at her. Every drop of blood seemed to have withdrawn its last faint red from her cheeks. She had even grown thinner and older, and she was bent up double, crying.

'Am I? *Am* I? Is that what you ask?'

The sound of her voice was as toneless and drear as some black stagnant pool fringed with muttering rushes in the flats of a marsh where a lost bird is lamenting what never can be uttered or understood. 'Well, what if I am? It's not *you* I am concerned with now. Not even *you* can divorce one's very soul from its memories. He is dead. And that—for you—is all that matters.'

'All? Indeed, poppet! And yet, supposing, I say, that being dead he yet speaketh?'

Fair, sleek face, rather long and partially hairless smooth head, glossy as dull brass, Aubrey continued to examine the human creature before him as carefully and coldly as if, ardent naturalist, he had brought down a bird of a rare species and was admiring its plumage. Well, it had always been a relief and refreshment to persecute her; even though this time he had gone far nearer the edge, and that irrevocably, than he had intended. Her misery was a kind of doglike joy to him. And why not? He was being persecuted himself! For jealousy, even if it is concerned with the despised and valueless, can be a bitter draught. Especially if one keeps on secretly sipping at the cup. Especially if . . . Yes, but—jealousy thrown in or not—would he never, never know whether or not this 'Mr Hamilton' of his had, or had *not,* decided to knock.

'You see, my dear Emily,' he went on, 'at the very mention—and, for God's sake, don't keep on crying, you know how it infuriates me— at the very mention of his name you let your emotions get the better of you. There's a word for it—hysteria. It's a sort of delayed green sickness—chlorosis. Ask Dr McLechlan. I don't blame you; though I am not so easy a victim myself to such little aberrations. Not *so* easy, I say; to be quite truthful. It merely occurred to me to ask the question. You see, you had already been brooding, preening your woes. I have lived with you long enough—oh, how long!—to recognize the æolian strains. And now a whole year has gone by; yes, to the very day. Surely that should have given you time enough to get really and truly used to things.'

The words were little more than sluggishly creeping out of his mouth, as though he were talking in his sleep.

'Don't flatter yourself,' he went on, 'that I am seething with any particular emotion. Envy, hatred, even uncharitableness; that kind of thing. I don't care a tinker's curse whether you were then, or are now, in love with him. These women! I don't *care,* I say. I was never anything more than 'second thoughts'; and then became Enemy No. 1. And yet, darling, I couldn't have let you go. Now, could I? Just headlong to your own ruin. Better the sop of sentimental memories after a year than, well, an even worse debacle. You have no notion what a canker a heartsick woman can be. Nor, darling, had he. And, unfortunate! He left us too early to find out. So be happy with

your treasured woes. Why, he looks in on you with every mouthful
of bread you eat. He flavours every sip of water. We don't wear
empty faces, sigh at nothing, look over our shoulders when there is
nobody, nothing there, just for fun. Bless you, no! You can take
that from *me*. . . . But—but, yet again, supposing there had been love
enough? As that pimp of futility ejaculated: "It is the cause, my soul;
it is the cause." Did you by any chance ever read the plays together—
and then "read no more"?'

Her face slowly turned in his direction, like a snail's groping from
its shell in search of its way. It was mottled and distorted with weeping.

'I haven't any notion,' she said, 'what has happened. What horror.
Why you are talking like this; what—what insanity has come over
you. All this vileness. It is never only what you say, but the in-
sinuations, the poisonous things underneath the words.' A shuddering
breath shook her whole body. 'Well, then, listen to me. I know that,
while we are together, I am at your mercy. We are husband and wife.
That was—and that, Heaven help me, still is and must be—the end of
that. But you have no right, before God or man, to question me like
this. Still, here I am, and, as far as I know, in my right mind, and I
will be quite candid with you. If, only *yesterday,* he *had* come back,
and had wanted me—are you listening?—then, whether he was living
or dead, I should have refused to see him. Why, you will ask. Because
then, I was past bearing it. Ours is ours, his is his, and mine is mine.
You merely filthed and made vile the most sacred misfortune the heart
can suffer and endure. You dragged it through your mud. For your
own poor shifty ends. Ends—though not from my choosing—unattainable now. We had said *our* goodbye, for ever. At least, for any ever
known on earth. And now, well . . . I take it back.'

'Take *what* back?' shouted Aubrey, as if the contempt and fury now
writhing on his dead-alive face were almost past endurance. 'Take
what back? With your rubber water-bottles and your furry slippers
and your grizzlings and your grousing! Haven't I a right to speak?
Haven't I a word to say? Take *what* back?' He had this time—as
if under the very blackness of the dry frozen forests—wolfishly yelled
the question; and suddenly at sound of it had been seized with a sort
of mental rigor. Good God! came the whisper, had his bodiless enemy
actually planned and timed his visit for this?

Emily had continued to look at, to watch him; her dark eyes, stupe-
fied with crying, shining out as if from a mask of bone. 'That "for
ever," ' she managed to whisper. 'I take *that* back. If now I thought

he wanted me, I'd . . . No,' she cried, pushing up her hands to her face, 'I cannot bear very much more. I know now something awful has happened. What is it? Who is it?'

*   *   *   *   *

In the pause that followed, a quiet tapping on the panel of the closed door interrupted them. Aubrey wheeled about as abruptly as an animal that has detected in its nocturnal ravaging the snapping of a twig. He turned and by a few inches gently opened the door.

'What is it?' he said. He was blankly searching the cold impassive face beyond it, sharply lit by the lamps of both bedroom and landing.

'If you please, sir,' said Mary, 'a Mr *Hamilton* has called. And, as you told me, I suppose it is about a picture. He stood there; and didn't speak. And after I inquired—well, I couldn't understand. The mouth moved, but I was not sure if . . . He seemed to have been waiting in the porch. Perhaps he had knocked before, and was listen-

ing. But there's, of course, the *bell*. And of course, Madam, I shut the door. You never know. . . .'

In spite of her 'Madam,' her black eyes were fixed on Aubrey's—wide-open and stonily pale-blue—while he tried in vain to keep his lips from trembling. It was as if she had accepted his challenge, even though her attention appeared to be elsewhere. He continued to scrutinize that queer facial chart, this human woman's, which because of its strength of purpose, of its honesty and integrity perhaps, he had never been able to decipher. Was this merely a trick? Was this a vindictive Mary resenting his pretences? *Was* anyone there? Was it merely some advertising tout? Some ticket-seller? An idiotic coincidence? Had he . . . ?

'As a matter of fact,' Mary began again, 'I had a feeling that he meant he wished to see, not you, Sir, but Madam.'

A remote yet devilish smile, expressing something between fear, astonishment, triumph and incredulity, was on Aubrey's face as he called back over his shoulder, 'Did you hear that, Emily? Someone for *you*. Someone has come for *you*.' Then he looked again ; but there was no answer.

'Thank you, Mary,' he managed to mutter at her, but not quite coherently. 'You were perfectly right to shut the door. *That* was no Mr Hamilton. Some wretched whining tramp, perhaps. He may be gone—by now. If not, say there is illness. No—' he violently shook his head—'don't open. Don't open, I say. No good, now. It is impossible.'

He said no more, but slowly shut the door on her, listened for the last rumour of her receding footsteps, and then, with exquisite caution, slowly turned the key.

He switched off the light, tip-toed to the window and, neatly and punctiliously as a woman, between finger and thumb drew aside the curtain and looked out, and down. Vaguely stirring soundless shadows of trees ; shafts of light and of shadow in the small square porch ; and nothing besides. Not pausing, even to breathe again, he silently pushed the window ajar, leaned out and looked again. No. . . . He pulled the window to, moistened his lips, pushed the hasp home and drew back the curtains ; and this so gently that the metal of curtain-ring scarcely sounded on brass rod. Yet again he listened ; then stepped back nimbly ; and switched on the light again. What *she* had heard he could not tell. She had fallen sideways along her bed ; her face between her outstretched arms, as curiously tranquil and composed as if she were already a stranger to all life's longings.

'Holy God!' he muttered.

Then he called, though almost inaudibly, across to her, 'Emily! Emily . . . what's wrong?'

But no effort could as yet persuade him to go near her. Not for him—not for himself then? But an anniversary! To keep an 'assignation'? And Jacob had had to wait *seven* years! How fatuous, how preposterous! Breathing so rapidly that a slight giddiness had swept over consciousness, he passed by her motionless body at as great a distance as the wall allowed, and lifted the telephone receiver from a small and pretty mahogany table that stood, innocent of any share in the proceedings, on the other side of the bed. With extreme deliberation, as if it were an achievement requiring the utmost skill, he dialled a number.

'Is that Dr. Webber's,' he inquired. . . . 'Thank you.'

He put his left hand over the mouthpiece and tried to control his breathing.

'Yes. Thank you. This is Mr Silcot, Mr Edmund Silcot. It is you, Dr Webber? Yes, thank you. Could you come? . . . Yes, now ; at once. I am afraid my wife is seriously ill. Only a fainting fit perhaps. Some kind of heart attack. I cannot say. We were talking quite as usual . . . " Just home?" I'm sorry. I know what that means. But yes ; it *is* rather urgent. Yes . . . Yes . . .'

He carefully returned the receiver to its slumber, drew back ; tip-toed round the bed, and began to listen again.

And in this transfixture, a single commonplace word came sallying nonchalantly up out of his memory as if it were hurt at its not having been duly noticed before—the word 'unattainable.' Heaven above us! What was *not* unattainable in this world! But *two* victories! A double event! Rage and despair, like a vortex of wind and rain, swept over his mind. The very bridge of his nose seemed to sharpen as presently he stooped over the bed—at a ridiculous corporeal right angle—and his face assumed a stonelike pallor. Slowly, and with the utmost gingerliness, refusing even to touch her pillow, he pushed down his lips close to the ear of his human companion and called softly—a voice cringing yet as ferocious as that of a wolf in the snow-bound mountains—and as though he had addressed it into the very centre of outer darkness, cold, callous and illimitable :

'Emily, Emily! Are you there? It's Aubrey. I am in a hell of a mess. . . . Hopeless. . . . What did you mean by "unattainable"? "un-at-tainable"?'

And again that slowly repeated tapping on the panel interrupted him. He crossed the room, and with exquisite caution released the catch in the door, holding this firmly a few inches open.

'What do you want now?' he asked.

'What's going on in there?' said the voice. 'Is the doctor coming?'

'The doctor?'

'Yes . . . And there hasn't been any knock again from that Mr Hamilton you said was about.'

'Oh,' he replied ; and was compelled for what seemed yet another infinitesimal yet protracted hole in Eternity to gaze palely back—searching the depths of the motionless black eyes that were fixed upon his own—before his tongue could utter another word.

Anthony Gilbert

Missing Gentleman

by *ADRIAN ALINGTON*

'As you may imagine, Inspector, my uncle's disappearance has cast quite a gloom over Christmas. I was obliged, of course, to cancel his Boxing Day party, though I concealed the real reason, merely giving out that my uncle was indisposed. Poor Uncle, he always enjoyed his Boxing Day party so much. And this year he was looking forward to it with particular eagerness.

'I last saw him on the night of Christmas Eve, five days ago. In his usual health and spirits? Yes, in a way. But, you know, Inspector, I really think it will be best for me to tell you the facts in my own way, even though some of them may seem irrelevant. The Boxing Day party, for instance, is probably quite important. My uncle, you know, is a very keen amateur conjurer—he is good enough to be a member

134

of the Magic Circle—and always gives a special performance at the party. It is one of the high spots of the year for him. He invites all the children in the neighbourhood. He is very fond of children, though he has always had an unhappy feeling that they are afraid of him, for, as you may know, the poor man has the misfortune to be dreadfully cross-eyed.

'Whether they are really afraid of him or not, they always love his party and particularly his conjuring entertainment. The shrieks of delight last year when he performed the familiar trick of bringing a rabbit out of his top hat! He keeps a rabbit, you know, especially to use in his tricks. We call him Joseph—Jo-Jo, for short,—and he lives in a hutch in the garden. We are both greatly attached to Jo-Jo.

'I don't know whether you know Major Horton-Gore by sight. He is a near neighbour of ours and an old friend of my uncle's. He dressed up as Father Christmas at the party last year and distributed presents from a sack. Unfortunately he too is an enthusiastic amateur conjurer, though he has never been elected to the Magic Circle, a fact which, I am afraid, has given birth to a streak of unworthy jealousy in an otherwise charming disposition.

'Conjurers, of course, never give one another away in public, but Major Horton-Gore, though, as I have said, a most amiable man, in other respects, seems to take a really unpleasant delight in telling my uncle before his audience that he can spot exactly how his tricks are worked. This know-all attitude infuriates my uncle, particularly as he always has to admit subsequently that the Major was perfectly right. Ridiculous as it may seem in two normally courteous and reasonable men, the Major and my uncle did not speak to one another for nearly six weeks after the party last year.

'About a month ago, I noticed that my uncle was becoming very thoughtful and absent-minded. There was nothing surprising about this. I knew that he was at work on the tricks which he was going to perform on Boxing Day, and from remarks he let drop, I guessed that he was fully determined to baffle Major Horton-Gore this year. He has a little room, you know, at the top of the house, which he calls his workroom, and where he keeps his properties and experiments with new tricks. He took to going up there immediately after dinner and remaining there far into the night.

'As Christmas approached, he grew increasingly excited and restless. I began to feel that I should be glad when Boxing Day was over and we could settle down to our normal placid life again.

'On Christmas Eve he was more on edge than ever. He did not go to his office, but spent the whole day in his workroom. At dinner he looked quite worn out, yet there was a strange glitter in his eye. He hardly touched his food, but talked feverishly between intervals of profound silence. This talk alarmed me, for he declared that the experiment which he had now almost completed would baffle not only Major Horton-Gore, but the pundits of the Magic Circle as well. In fact, he assured me quite seriously, there was no trick for anyone to discover. For, by dint of ferocious concentration, he had at last advanced beyond the bounds of mere legerdemain into the realms of pure magic. He had always believed such a thing possible and now he of all men had been privileged to achieve it. He even talked of giving up business altogether and devoting the rest of his life to the development of his new powers.

'It seemed to me that he was on the brink of a nervous breakdown. I implored him to go to bed, but he grew quite angry, saying that I was under-estimating the crowning achievement of his life, and it was a mistake to tell a woman anything. As soon as dinner was over, he went straight back to his workroom. That was the last time I saw my uncle.

'Yes, of course, Inspector, I will answer any questions that you think necessary. I am only too anxious to have the dear old chap back again. But really I think it will save time if, first of all, you will come with me.'

Well, to humour this talkative young lady, I got up and went with her into the garden. There, just by the back door, was a rabbit hutch with two rabbits inside. 'The one on the left,' said the young lady, 'is Jo-Jo.' She called his name softly, then picked up a piece of lettuce and tickled it through the wire to attract the attention of the second rabbit. The creature turned and looked at us.

'You see what I mean, Inspector?' she said.

I did indeed. Honestly it gave me quite a turn. It wasn't so much the mournfulness of the gaze as—well, I never remember to have seen a cross-eyed rabbit before.

Three Wise Men

by *JOANNA CANNAN*

Illustrated by Sarah Nechamkin

SUSAN and Dick had married early, Susan at twenty-one and Dick at twenty. 'Just a couple of mad kids,' Susan would say. Now in their early thirties they possessed a neat little house in a garden city and a carefully planned family of three boys, a couple of years between each of them. The slowness of Dick's promotion in the Civil Service was offset, Susan said, by its sureness—you could plan ahead—and with Brian and Ian at the nearby progressive non-profit-making co-educational day school, the baby, three year old Richard, at a nursery school, and Maria, a Displaced Person, in the kitchen, Susan had been able to resume her secretarial work in a political organization, with the aims of which she fervently sympathized. The snag was the school holidays; the nursery school was still available for Richard, and Maria was perfectly prepared to take charge of Brian and Ian—plain fat middle-aged though she was, the boys adored her—but Maria's ideas on child-management were not Susan's : Maria, though an excellent cook, was no dietitian ; ignorant and obtuse, she was unable to grasp the significance of vitamin content ; she was shocked to death by the chilly cereals and meagre salads

137

on which the Burnett family were scientifically nourished, and behind Susan's back she stuffed the boys with cakes and pastries, ingredients for which she would buy with her own money. Susan suspected, too, the influence of her backward and superstitious nature on their growing minds. It was difficult to estimate her command of English ; she often misinterpreted some simple order of Susan's, but seemed able to amuse the boys with a succession of silly old-fashioned stories of animals that talked, good and bad fairies. She was a devout Catholic and though Susan had from the first made it plain that she and her husband were atheists, that none of her babies had been subjected to the voodoo of christening, that any attempt to proselytize would mean instant dismissal, she felt with unease some warm dark aura diffused by the personality of this humble dispossessed and insignificant woman, some threat, gentle and insidious, to the white light, bald truth, pure reason, the atmosphere of which she had created in her home. Time and again she resolved to replace Maria with some intelligent woman with her own progressive ideas, but the few women whom she would have liked to employ stood out for help with the rough work, and the garden city bred no Calibans. So Maria stayed on and scrubbed and washed and ironed and cooked and gardened and knitted and sang tunelessly of talking bears and dwarfs in the forests and padded about the house barefoot—not in the laudable cause of physical culture, but to save her shoes.

Before the birth of their children the Burnetts had decided to forgo the farce that a conventional Christmas is to those who are not Christians, but later on the piteous lispings of their eldest boy, as he became aware of the new toys, the shining trees, the parties and the crackers enjoyed at this season by luckier children, reduced them to a compromise : in future there would be presents for the children, a fowl on the table, perhaps even a tree, electrically lighted but devoid of religious emblems. Crackers were banned. They had no religious significance, but contained trash, and Susan detested trash : excepting sports equipment, she disapproved of all toys without a sound educational value.

Well before Christmas, she explained all this to Maria ; the previous year the servant, then a newcomer, had bought each of the boys a cheap card, which had been quickly thrown down and forgotten, but she was now so devoted to the boys and had, her employers reckoned, saved so much money, that Susan, who was not without feeling, feared the embarrassment of having to deal both honestly and kindly with a collection of utterly unsuitable presents. Maria received Susan's generalities with silence and an occasional shrug ; but Susan was confronted by the discovery that Maria had taken to locking the door of her little bed-sitting-room behind her. 'She's knitting for them,' said Susan.

When Christmas morning came, Susan arranged the boys' presents on the breakfast table. From his parents Brian received an elementary chemistry set ; Ian, Engineero. For Richard there was a box of interlocking plastic bricks, which would train his hands to neatness. The grandparents had cautiously sent Savings Certificates. Susan sighed with relief. No trash, thank goodness.

Susan and Dick still kept their pact and gave one another no presents, but they had each a parcel to open. Dick's contained a pair of socks and Susan's an elaborately patterned jersey. Called from the kitchen to be thanked, Maria beamed. 'And you boys, you t'ink I forget you? No, nevaire. In ze sitting-room is somesing I make for you.' As the boys rushed off, she added, 'Chust a toy, such as we make in my contry.'

Susan and Dick followed their sons into the living-room, and found the curtains drawn against the hard light of the winter morning, the centre light switched off and a table lamp adjusted to shine on a straw-thatched stable under a tinsel star, a celluloid Babe, a plaster Mother, an ox and ass of lead, and against a backcloth of blue,

approaching camels. Before the representation, contained in an up-
ended apple-box, the three little boys kept an enchanted silence.

'Oh dear,' said Susan.

'I'll handle this,' Dick told her. 'Well, boys, so that's what Maria's
made you. A kind of dolls'-house, only fit for girls, of course, but she
meant well and you must thank her nicely.'

Brian said, 'It's not a dolls'-house. It's *Once in Royal David's City,*
like we heard on the radio.'

'And *Nowell, Nowell,*' said Ian.

'That's right—just a Children's Hour story,' said Susan, and Dick,
moving across the room to draw back the curtains, said, 'They know
that. They're no fools. Now cut along, all of you, and thank Maria
and don't hurt her feelings by letting her guess that you think it's a
silly present—she'll be out this afternoon, so she won't know that you
haven't played with it—and then we'll all go for a good brisk walk up
to the Community Centre. . . .'

Apparently Maria had misunderstood what Susan had told her
about Christmas dinner: she had made a pudding and, as Susan
detested waste, it was eaten instead of the Weetjerm biscuits and Vita-
creem cheese, which should have followed the chicken. After the meal
Susan and Dick began to feel sleepy; they yawned; uncontrollably
their eyelids drooped; after all, they were office workers, unaccustomed
to as much fresh air as they had imbibed this morning. Sprawling
and snoozing in a living-room was a thing that Susan detested, so they
placed a guard before the fire, told the boys to play quietly with their
presents and went upstairs to rest under the artificial silk eiderdowns
of their Eesielye twin beds.

It was four o'clock when Susan wakened. 'The boys *have* been
good. I didn't hear a sound,' she remarked as she combed her hair.
'They're absorbed with their toys,' Dick said, yawning. 'They're con-
structive toys, that's why. They occupy the mind and at the same
time satisfy the urge for achievement. I wonder what they've made
with the Engineero?' 'Something jolly good, I expect,' said Susan.
'Ian is a born engineer.'

They went downstairs. The living-room curtains were drawn. The
centre light was switched off, the table light was adjusted so that it
shone on the stable in Bethlehem. Before the crib knelt the three boys,
each cloaked in a chair-back.

Tripping over the unopened box of Engineero, Susan switched on
the light. 'Brian, Ian, whatever are you doing?'

'We're fwee wise men,' lisped Richard.

The Barber's Parrot

by GERALD BULLETT

Illustrated by Laurence Scarfe

WHAT got into the papers wasn't the half of it (said my pub acquaintance). Look at it this way : what would *you* do if you were a young man and someone stole your girl, and that someone a whey-faced elderly barber? Try and get her back? You bet. But suppose she wouldn't come? Suppose she said she was fond of her husband and wouldn't leave him or deceive him, not for all the tea in China? You'd see red then, I fancy ; and if you were fool enough you'd knock her out, let's say, and have done with it. But you're not a fool. You're clever. You think things out and you spy a better way. A drop of poison in the ear, a word in season, and if all goes well you get the rough work done for you, and the other fellow pays the penalty. Two birds with one stone.

The story begins, for you and me, when the foreign-looking sailorman marches into Sparkfield's shop with a parrot perched on his shoulder and a birdcage dangling from his hand. It was here in Rookhaven it all happened. Sparkfield was more or less a newcomer to the town, and knowing no better he'd had the old name taken down and *Sparkfield's Tonsorial Saloon* put up in its place. Quite a snug concern, and nicely situated. From the bit of garden at the back, where young Mrs Sparkfield hung out her week's washing, you could see right down to the quay and watch the tall ships coming and going.

'Haircut,' said Sparkfield, 'or shave?'

'Nice bright day, Mr Sparkfield,' said the sailorman.

He was foreign-looking because of his curly black hair and his tanned skin. He wore a large jewelled ring on his first finger ; he brought with him a smell of tar and old ropes ; he had a trick of screwing up his small bright eyes, sharp as glass, as though looking at you in strong sunlight or from a long distance. But the tune of his speech, racy and musical, with a salt singsong tang to it, was English enough, and West Country at that.

'Just in from foreign parts?' said Sparkfield, always ready for a chat.

'Near enough,' said the stranger. For Sparkfield had never seen him before. 'You've a pretty little crib here, mister.'

'Glad you like it,' said Sparkfield.

'Me,' said the stranger, 'I'm looking for a home.'

'We don't take lodgers,' said Sparkfield. 'Haircut, shave, shampoo,

141

face massage. That's our line. Beauty treatment too, but you'll not be wanting that, I fancy.'

'Meaning?' said the stranger, narrowing his eyes to gimlet points.

'Smart young fellow like you,' said Sparkfield, laughing uneasily.

'I'm looking for a home,' said the stranger. 'For this parrot of mine,' he added.

'That's different,' Sparkfield conceded.

He saw that he had been hasty. His nerves, always on the jump nowadays, had betrayed him again. That's what comes of marrying a girl half your age. No fool like an old fool, they say, and poor Sparkfield had got it badly. He had been fifteen years a widower when he first saw Ella Marley, and all the dry tinder of his heart went up in a great blaze. He had felt like a boy again, a green boy, seeing the beauty of woman for the first time. But he wasn't a boy. He was a man of substance, in a nice way of business, and Ella a young woman sick and tired of waiting for an absentee lover who seemed to have forgotten all about her. Sparkfield didn't know that, but it would have made no difference if he had ; for during the weeks of courting he had lived in a sort of fever. She liked him. She loved him. She made him feel like a two-year-old. And he soon got into the way of not looking too long in the glass and of not believing what he saw there. Being shortsighted was a help. And it's quite easy to shave yourself with your eyes shut, once you get the trick of it, specially if shaving is your trade.

'Pretty Poll,' said the sailorman. 'He's a knowing old bird.'

Sparkfield listened nervously, one ear cocked towards the little parlour at the back of the shop, where perhaps Ella was at this very minute. His marriage was a delight and a torment. She was all that a man could wish for, and more precious than a man could imagine. But how to secure his treasure from prying eyes, from thieving fingers : that was his secret worry. Like an ingrowing toenail it was. He got the silly fancy that everyone was plotting to get her away from him. Now and again, in spite of his hints, she'd look in while he was at work and pass the time of day with a customer. He dreaded these visits, because he hated to see her smiling at another man ; yet if she didn't put in an appearance at least once during the morning he'd grow fretful, and begin to wonder, and at last, with a muttered apology to whoever was occupying the seat of execution, he would slip into the house to find her, cover her pretty face with kisses, and assure himself that she still belonged to him.

'Believe it or not,' said the sailorman, 'I paid a golden sovereign for this parrot.'

'Really? Haven't seen one of them since a boy,' said Sparkfield. 'What, parrots?'

'Golden sovereigns,' said Sparkfield. 'Is it a shave?' he asked, nodding at the empty chair. 'Or a haircut?'

The sailorman came nearer, jerking his thumb towards the bird on his shoulder.

'Take a look at him, mister. A man's best friend. I'm not asking money for him. Just a kind home, that's all. A lovely line of talk, and the habits of a gentleman.'

At that Sparkfield began to take notice of the parrot, feeling a bit easier. It was a handsome bird, still as an image and bright as new paint, like a child's toy. More like a painted ornament than something alive, so that when it did actually move its head half an inch, and cock a cold wicked eye at Sparkfield, he could hardly believe it.

'Pretty Poll,' said Sparkfield. 'You're certainly a fine-looking chap.'

'You've said it, mister. And I'll tell you another thing. There's nothing this bird misses. And nothing he won't tell, in his own time. What goes on, says you, in that brain-pan of his? Plenty's the answer. Plenty. Whatever goes on, he picks it up. Picks it up, stores it away, and there it is, all filed for reference. No secrets from him.'

'He hasn't said a word yet,' said Sparkfield.

'Treat him proper, he'll do the same by you. All in good time, out it comes. Good as a watchdog. Better, because a watchdog can't talk.'

'I wouldn't call *him* talkative,' said Sparkfield, getting tired of the sales-patter.

'Ship ahoy,' said the parrot suddenly.

Sparkfield stared, his eyes bulging.

'Plum duff in the cook's galley,' said the parrot. 'Devilish pretty woman.'

The sailor smiled. A cocky, superior smile. 'See what I mean? Nice company for the lady.'

'Lady?' said Sparkfield sharply.

'*Mrs* Sparks,' said the sailor. 'If so be there *is* such.'

There was. And at that moment, just when she was least wanted, she came bouncing in from the private quarters, bright as a new penny. I say bouncing, but you musn't think she was one of your big hearty wenches. Slim she was, graceful as a kitten, and so delicious to look at it made your heart turn to water.

'Well?' said Sparkfield, with a sick look. 'What is it now?'

His tone took her aback, as well it might. 'Nothing particular.
Didn't know you had company.'

'Good morning, miss," said the sailorman. 'How d'you like my
parrot?'

'Very nice, I'm sure,' said she.

Her manner was off-hand. Sparkfield was glad to see that she
showed no interest, either in the parrot or its owner.

'Right you are,' said the sailorman, all bright and breezy. 'He's
yours, lady. A little present from over the seas.'

With that he coaxes the bird into its cage, and sets the cage down
in the barber's smooth white wash-basin.

'That makes two of 'em,' he said, indicating the second parrot in the
mirror.

Before either Sparkfield or Ella could find anything to say he was
on his way out.

'Good as gold that bird is,' he said, pausing at the door. 'Your
Dad's taken quite a fancy to him, missy.'

II

You'll perhaps not believe that a grown man would let a little thing
like that worry him? But that only shows you didn't know Sparkfield. Old enough to be her father was a thought he'd had often
enough ; but hearing it said out loud like that, and by a perfect
stranger, made it worse, made it somehow more real. And said, what's
more, to *her*! Putting ideas into her head!

It was the first shot, you may say, in the campaign against his
peace of mind. It lodged in a vital spot and the wound festered.

The parrot, that wily old bird, made himself quite at home. Quite
a character he was. Didn't give a damn. It was all one to him where
he lived and who he lived with. His best friend couldn't have called
him sociable. Sometimes he'd answer when you spoke to him, and
sometimes he wouldn't. Sometimes what he said was just nonsense,
and sometimes it was so dead on the point it seemed uncanny. Left
to himself, Sparkfield might have got quite a lot of amusement out
of him. It was Ella's attitude that put him off. She, from the first,
stubbornly refused to take any interest in the creature. Almost as
though she'd got a grudge against it. This wasn't like Ella, a cheerful
little thing she was in the ordinary way, always ready for a bit of
innocent fun ; and it puzzled Sparkfield, and set him thinking. As the
days went by, he kept remembering her unnatural, off-hand manner
with the young fellow from the sea ; and the more he remembered it

the less he liked it. At the time it had seemed all right, better than all right. But now he began to imagine things.

'That young fellow. Ever seen him before?'

'Me? No,' said Ella. 'Why should I have?'

'Thought you might have,' said Sparkfield. Her answer made him more suspicious than ever. 'Seeing he's a local chap.'

'Who says he's a local chap?' Ella demanded.

He had set his trap, and she had walked into it. He pounced.

'Who are we talking about?' he said sharply.

She went very red. She looked both frightened and mutinous. 'Well, who are we? You ought to know.'

'And so do you know. Don't you?' She didn't answer. 'Don't you?' he said again.

Her eyes opened very wide. They were big eyes, blue as heaven. But there was fear in them and it maddened him.

'What's come over you, dear?' she said.

'Never mind the soft soap. Answer my question.'

Trying to fool me, he thought. But I wasn't born yesterday. Old enough to be her father.

'What question?'

'I asked you had you seen him before. You said, No you hadn't. Who, that's the question. Who haven't you seen before?'

'The man in the moon,' said Ella. The shop-bell tinkled. 'There's a customer. Better ask him.'

That was the beginning of real trouble between them. The subject wasn't referred to again, until the very end ; they tried to behave with each other as though nothing out of the way had happened ; but underneath all the everyday talk about this and that, there was a sort of silence. Suspicion on one side and fear on the other. Underneath the talk, and underneath the lovemaking too. For Sparkfield didn't dare to stop pestering and kissing her. If once he stopped he'd have lost her : that was how he looked at it. But of course it wasn't the same. Up to now she'd been an affectionate girl, no cause for complaint. But now, with her nerves on edge the way they were, she seemed timid, reluctant, almost shrinking. You can guess what that did to Sparkfield. It was crystal clear to him that she didn't like him any more. It seemed that he gave her the creeps. Maybe he was right up to a point, but it wasn't for the reason he thought.

A girl, you may say, once safely married, can always send an impudent young fellow about his business, no matter what she may have promised him years ago. 'Bygones is bygones,' she can say. 'I'm sticking to my bargain, and no nonsense from you.' But what if he won't *be* sent? What if he's bent on making mischief for mischief's sake? And the devil's own mischief at that.

Day after day, day after day. Things went from bad to worse. Nothing more said. Just small talk and surface smiles and a creeping poison. The parrot's cage, I ought to tell you, was hung up in the little parlour, behind the shop. Next to the parlour was the kitchen quarters, beyond them the bit of garden, and beyond that a green slope to the sea, which you could get at, if you were so minded, through a door in the fence. I say was, but it still is : I'll take and show you any day you like.

III

Sparkfield's talks with the parrot didn't help, either. He did, in a way, make a friend of the parrot, for he couldn't get it out of his head that the parrot was in the know. In the know about what?

'Ship ahoy,' said the parrot. '*What* a nice man!'

'Who is?' said Sparkfield. 'Eh, Polly?'

'Scratch a poll,' said the parrot. 'Busy Saturday.'

That made Sparkfield stare. It sounded like magic. Because, of course, Saturday afternoon *was* his busiest time, with the shop full of haircuts. It was nothing much in itself, but it just went to show what a knowing old bird the parrot was.

'What's going on, I wonder?' said the parrot. 'Silly old sinner.'

That was just what Sparkfield wanted to know too. Why was Ella always so late back from her shopping nowadays? And why had she taken to using the back way, instead of coming through the shop?

Well, I won't keep you in suspense any longer. You know something of what happened. You've seen it in the papers. It was the anonymous letters that did the trick in the end. We can guess the kind of thing, can't we? Little drops of poison from an Unknown Friend, or some such blarney. It's my belief that those letters were written by the same hand as the one that arrived for Ella herself. He would have opened it if he'd had a chance, but she was too quick for him. She put on an act. Said it was from her Aunt Maudie. But he had seen the postmark, and the postmark was Rookhaven. When he demanded to see the letter she said she'd torn it up. But she hadn't and she didn't. She didn't have time. It was found, afterwards, by the police. And it put a noose round a man's neck.

If only she hadn't been afraid of him, all would have been well.

The truth wouldn't have hurt her, or him either. Or not much. Funny
things, human beings, when you come to think of it.

So we come to that last morning. He'd had next to no sleep for
days. He'd lain there, fretting and tossing and turning in the dark,
with Ella at his side sleeping or pretending to sleep. He'd stare at her
by the hour together, and take my word for it, she was as pretty as a
picture. It was torture for Sparkfield, and deep inside him, though I
don't think he knew it yet, was murder. If *he* couldn't have her, no
one else should. He wasn't the only one that was feeling like that.
And when two men get that idea about a girl, her number's up, poor
thing.

Within a few minutes of that bit of conversation about Aunt
Maudie's letter, what should he hear but a noise, coming from the
parlour. The sound of a man's voice. He heard it because, if you ask
me, he was meant to hear it. There was no one else in the shop at
the time. Sparkfield was busy stropping a razor.

Laughter from the back parlour, and a man's voice. He tiptoed to
the door, turned the handle, looked in.

She was alone, deathly pale, visibly terrified. Her eyes grew bigger
and bigger as she met his flaming stare.

'Well, where is he?' Her terror maddened him the more.

She shook her head dumbly, unable to utter a sound. His wild
glance lit on something that lay on the floor. A sailor's cap, with a
ship's name round the rim in gold letters.

In a white fury he picked it up and handed it to her.

'Kiss me again, dear,' said the parrot.

And so he cut her throat. Just like that. One appalling spasm of
violence, and there she was, dead, and he—worse than dead. Or that's
how I see it. And as he stands there in a sort of paralysed frenzy,
trying not to believe what he has done, back comes Jimmie the sailorman, stepping in from the kitchen quarters. At sight of him the
madness broke out again. Sparkfield sprang at him, razor in hand.
In the struggle he got his face slashed open with his own razor, which
Jimmie twisted out of his grip. The next thing he knew was a punch
in the eye, and Jimmie making off, taking the razor with him.

Sparkfield was left alone with his dead.

'Ship ahoy,' said the parrot. 'Ain't she a beauty!'

IV

The plan had worked perfectly. Jimmie the sailorman, that crafty
and all-conquering young fellow, had had his way. He'd driven Spark-

field dotty and brought death and damnation into his home. But he'd made one trifling miscalculation; for Sparkfield, as it turned out, was crafty too, in his fashion. Sparkfield said, quite simply, that Jimmie had done it. Said he caught him, razor in hand, and grappled with him, and got a slashed face for his pains. And when you come to think of it, what more likely? There was Jimmie's letter to support the story. 'I'm not letting anyone else have you, so make up your mind to it.' Sparkfield's own sentiments in reverse, don't you see? Funny, isn't it? That letter did Jimmie no good. What's more, he'd been seen by a neighbour entering and leaving by the back way; his finger-prints were found on the razor; and he'd made the mistake of trying to run away.

So there you are. Knowing no better they hanged Jimmie, leaving Sparkfield to make his own arrangements. Which he did. He had only one thing left to wait for, and when that was accomplished he made his exit. Within an hour of Jimmie's execution he committed a sort of suicide by vanishing from the district and putting it about that he was dead: so much is common knowledge. As for the rest, you may take it or leave it, but that's how it was. Who should know better than I?

Who *am* I, do you say? The late Mr Sparkfield, at your service.

Insomnia

by JOHN PUDNEY

Illustrated by Susan Einzig

A s it went on and on, and the days grew longer, Sophy's sleeplessness became more and more of a problem. Not only did it
distress the family for her sake, but also because it looked like
endangering Mother's health and indeed the very financial structure
of life at Number Ten.

These thoughts worried Sophy and made her sleep even worse. Her
only real calling was to look after Mother, though the typewriting she
did was also a basic material contribution to their existence. Without
it, Mother's fixed income would go nowhere, as the family often pointed
out, and Sophy would just not be pulling her weight. In any case, it
was the only work for which she was trained, and heaven knows what
would happen to her in the end if she did not possess some kind of
livelihood. This *end,* they spoke of, referred to Mother's death, an
event mercifully as remote as doomsday itself.

So the typewriting was a bread-and-butter necessity, not a mission
in life: and when Sophy did not sleep, she wondered what would
happen to Mother if anything happened to her. She might have done
better, and possibly even enjoyed it a little, if she had continued to go
out to work. That, however, would have meant Mother being alone
at Number Ten all day and every day, with nobody to answer the
door or chase after the daily woman to make sure she did her work.
Mother would have had to live like a hermit, too, unable even to have
anybody in for a chat in the afternoons without overtaxing herself and
feeling giddy. The doctor agreed that it was better for Sophy to work
at home—so long as her eternal 'tappity-tap,' as he called it, did not
disturb Mother.

For her insomnia, as soon as it began to get on Mother's nerves, he
prescribed various tonics and pills. He diagnosed it in turn as being
caused by indigestion, anaemia, overwork and selfish worry. Sophy
tried to explain that her only worry was what might happen to
Mother if anything happened to her: but the family and the doctor
ridiculed the thought.

If she could have worked for a few hours at night, she often thought,
sleep might have come easier. The tappity-tap in itself, together with
the assurance that her wakefulness was bringing in money, might well
have induced a slumber of at least material contentment. But the

sound of a typewriter at night anywhere in that substantial house wore
Mother's nerves to shreds. Even in her sleep, Mother could sense it.
Though it might not wake her up, it caused bad dreams. Sophy's
activities, therefore, had been restricted to the usual office hours of
nine till six. Within these limits, and those of the daily tasks entailed
in looking after Mother, she managed the regular flow of work
which came to her from an agency. She managed well, in fact, until
that year when her sleeplessness began with the snowdrops.

At Number Ten, they were always aware of the seasons because of
the old square garden at the back which Mother loved and Sophy
tended. The garden was a part of the security of Number Ten. Everybody in the family remembered it, the fusty smell of box edging in the
hot sun, the evening fragrance of stocks, the exuberance of the pink
chrysanthemums relishing the bitter town soil and autumnal days fore-
shortened by Nature's mist and the smoke from the railway cutting at
the end of the road. Mother doted on the garden. It would kill her
to give up Number Ten and live in a flat with no place of her own in
which to potter.

Number Ten was admittedly too large for the two of them. Its
chores were beyond the capacity of the daily woman. Certain rooms
had to be closed up. Nevertheless it was a fortress in a neighbourhood
of changing values, in a suburb which had gone down. But for the
doctor's, Number Ten was the only house in the street which had not
been converted into flats. It was Sophy's competence at the keyboard
which had kept those faded red blinds in the front windows, which
had preserved the single door-bell in all that row of houses with
multiple door-bells. And what would happen, Sophy asked herself, as
the evenings drew out and she rarely slept till first light, if this competence failed?

'Perhaps,' the doctor said, frowning toward the lilacs, 'it is more
fresh air that you need. You've got a garden. Try walking about in
it when you can't sleep. So long as you don't wake your Mother. . . .'

'I'm used to moving about the house without disturbing her. I'm
sure I could slip into the garden, though, of course, I've never tried.'

'Its Nature's own remedy—better than all the pills in the world.'
The doctor said it convincingly. Though he only brought in Nature
as a last resort, he meant what he said.

It was upon his advice, therefore, that Sophy emerged when the
moon was waxing and shook the urban dew from the lilacs. Behind
her stood Number Ten, familiar and solid, homely and impregnable ;
but denying her sleep. She turned to look up at it, at the dark cavern

Susan Einzig.

152

of Mother's open window rhythmically haunted by heavy breathing, at her own room, above, where the pink bedside light glowed, at the other windows whose closed and curtained emptiness caught the light of the moon. It was strange to reflect that men had once lived behind those windows—Father, brothers who had grown into strangers or died, brothers' and sisters' friends who had been polite during some brief, usually purposeful, sojourn. Sometimes they came back—but only for tea. They never stayed. Sometimes, like Father, they never came back.

And now it was funny to think of Number Ten with men in it.

Sophy smiled as she skirted the rockery and walked to the end of the garden to see the moon through the poised plumes of the white lilac. White lilac amid that urban pattern of houses. How lucky they were, as Mother always said, though careful pruning had had much to do with it. Sophy stepped up on to the garden roller the better to lean her elbows on the garden wall as she had done so often in—what was it?—the thirty-eight or thirty-nine years of life at Number Ten. The doctor had been right in this at least. If one had to be sleepless, to hold back the whispering summonses of anxiety, to beat off the nagging company of loneliness, it was better outdoors. It was soothing to see the familiar, so magicked by that majestic yet somehow frivolous light. It was thieving back a little of the time which had been claimed by worry.

She rested her elbows on top of the wall. The familiar rough edge of the brickwork was now exquisitely moist and cool, as if the dew upon it were really silver. She smiled again because her sense of loneliness had drifted away and the summons of anxiety was drowned by the small noises of a breeze in the acacia in the next garden where in the daytime the offspring of these families bickered. Over the wall at the end of the garden, she was facing the back gardens of Nassau Avenue, and, beyond, the tall houses reaching up, grey and moon-spangled, into the uncrowded sky. She smiled and lowered her eyes : and in doing so she looked down smiling into the averted face of a man.

It could only be the dentist at Number Ten in Nassau Avenue, she realized that. Mother's information was correct and up-to-date in matters of that sort. The new dentist who had moved into the locality when it had begun to go down in order to cash in, so Mother understood, upon the new class of catch-as-catch-can resident. 'Poor Nassau Avenue!' Mother had said. 'It was always second best, but who would have thought that it could have sunk to dentists.'

With this awareness upon her like a flash, Sophy noticed that the

H

man was smiling up at her in a surprised way and that his face possessed the symmetrical beauty and physical tranquillity of a knight. A knight, that is, such as she in the long placid years of her devotion at Number Ten had come to conjure up. An idealized creature to whom loneliness was unknown. A being beyond the calls of anxiety. One to whom the gift of sleep was a natural and regular benison.

The dentist looked like that, perhaps because of the moonlight and his surprise at seeing her. The fact that he was wearing a pyjama top over a pair of army slacks—a get-up he would not care to be seen dead in—was of no momentary consequence to either of them.

'How wonderful of you,' he said, without so much as a hint of introduction, 'to step into my dream.'

'Are you asleep then?' she said, with a mixture of disappointment and envy.

'For the first time for weeks, I feel delighted to be awake,' said he, never taking his eyes off her, making no attempt whatever to conceal the delighted surprise which, combined with the moonlight, so transformed him and enchanted her.

'You mean you don't like being awake?' she heard herself saying— some dream-self, rare, full of sagacity, whispering in an effortless understanding of the knight who stood beneath the wall looking up.

'I can't sleep,' he whispered, his curving, strongly-marked eyebrows wavering as his dark eyes blinked in the magic light which hid the pink bruise where in the hours of daylight spectacles bridged his nose.

'But I can't sleep,' she whispered back, her greying hair turned to amber framed in the trembling lilac. 'I can't sleep either.'

The clocks of London, down below on the other side of the railway cutting, mentioned the quarters of the small hours : but neither he nor she moved. The wall was the altar upon which a marriage of their insomnia was motionlessly, timelessly, celebrated.

After a long time the dentist broke off an overhanging plume of lilac, kissed it and said : 'I shall keep this until tomorrow.' He stifled a yawn gracefully. 'Perhaps I shall keep it for ever.'

'For ever,' she said, taking one of the clusters from his plume, delicately so that not even the tips of their fingers touched. 'Let's both keep it for ever.'

She watched him trying to cram the blossom in the ridiculously small pocket of his pyjama jacket. She felt the silvery chill of her piece where her prudent pink woolly held it against her breasts. Ten minutes later she was asleep in bed.

In the morning, of course, she was even more tired than usual, and

Mother, in spite of her own cold, mentioned it to the doctor. 'The night air is never going to do her any good. Walking about in the garden with the heavy dew. . . . Look at the bags under her eyes.'

'But the doctor's right,' Sophy said serenely, 'when he calls it Nature's own remedy. I believe I shall sleep.' She looked across the assembled bric-à-brac of Mother's drawing-room to the long windows which offered a glimpse of distant white lilac.

'Let's give Nature a chance, then, and risk the dew,' said the doctor cautiously. 'so long as nobody is disturbed.'

'I shan't disturb Mother,' Sophy murmured out of the soft pre-occupation which descended upon her senses, with the contentment of late spring rain.

That contentment carried her through the day and to bed at ten o'clock—that routine bed-time to which Mother nodded with healthy drowsiness, which Sophy approached with an aching crescendo of alert-ness. 'If you can't get off, my dear,' Mother said sleepily, 'you'll have to try the garden again. . . .'

Whether sleep followed or not, going to bed as soon as Mother had settled down, was, of course, a habit. It was also a necessary pre-liminary to any cure for sleeplessness. Sophy turned off the pink bedside light. She did this partly for a sight of the moon and the distant glimpse of white lilac : but partly lest it should be interpreted as an unworthy signal by the knight whose yellowing cluster of lilac she fondled as she lay back on her pillow to await the positive summons of insomnia.

But for the customary panting of a goods train in the cutting, the dark breathing of Mother downstairs and the leafy noises of the acacia in the next garden, the urban night was already still as Sophy stretched and reached her arms back to place her token where it should not be crushed in the alcove at her bed-head. After that, she knew no more then until the astonishment of the morning sun gently prised open her eyelids and Mother's bell shrilled querulously below.

In Mother's room, wearing her prudent pink woolly, she lit the gas to make tea and confessed that she had overslept. 'There's no need to blush about that,' Mother said. 'You owe it all to the good sense of the doctor. If you had had your own way, no doubt you'd still be swallowing pills and potions.'

Sophy did not argue or apologize. As she tried to check her blushes, she came all too near to tears. The contentment she had felt the evening before had not left her. It had indeed been refreshed by deep sleep. To that extent her need was for happy tears. Yet there was also the sweet sadness of that broken tryst beneath the white lilacs. She could not help thinking of the patient knight alone there in the moonlight, the idealized creature who no doubt was the Nassau Avenue dentist, whose dark eyes had blinked in the magic light as he had placed the lilac in the pocket of his pyjama jacket.

As she bent over the teapot, not answering or even hearing Mother's routine morning comments, she indulged in a douce exultation of her own. He would be there at the bottom of the garden, she told herself, again and again. And all the balmy nights of the summer were still to come!

'Do look what you're doing, Sophy dear! You seem to be still half asleep,' Mother snorted. 'It's wasting gas to let a kettle boil away like that.'

Sophy enjoyed her lonely work at the typewriter that day. Instead of wearily driving away all thoughts of night, she allowed her mind to wander deliciously toward the prospect of night after night of gentle wakefulness by the silvery altar of the garden wall.

The lilac token in her alcove withered and yet the joys of her tryst were postponed night after night by the effortless slumber of her new contentment. Mother noticed her early morning preoccupation and, after a day or two, mentioned it to the doctor. Mother called it 'unhealthy drowsiness,' excusing herself for referring to it by saying that it was always as well to be on the safe side.

'That,' the doctor said, 'is simply Nature's way and I think we need do no more than to suggest a little vigorous application of cold water. But at least, Sophy, we're getting a good night's sleep?'

'I've been sleeping excellently, almost too . . .' Sophy stopped herself, just in time, from expressing the rather pleasant sense of guilt she felt in the continued postponement of her tryst.

'There's a lot to be said for Nature's remedy,' the doctor said, blowing out his cheeks, and gazing thoughtfully down the garden toward the skyline of Nassau Avenue. 'That little dentist, for instance. Very overworked, unmarried, no real worries. . . .' Mother loved the doctor's little matrimonial jokes. 'No family ties like you, Sophy . . . just working for his living . . . couldn't sleep a wink. There's a case of Nature's own remedy too. Funnily enough I saw him only this morning. He's been sleeping like a top.'

'Don't laugh like that, Sophy,' said Mother, 'I'm sure there's nothing *funny* about that. It makes you sound almost hysterical.'

'I'm sorry,' Sophy said, 'I'm just happy.'

Memoirs of a Batman

Illustrated by Edward Ardizzone

We have a weakness for specialized and out-of-the-way journals, and we recently made a most rewarding discovery in the pages of the journal of the Royal Pioneer Corps. Amongst the conventional contents was a contribution from an ex-batman, now a barrow-boy in London, which seemed to us to speak the authentic language of the 'old sweat.' By permission of the Editor, and by way of a tribute to one of the most necessary if least glamorous branches of the British Army, we print some reminiscences of 'Ex-Batman,' who insists on anonymity. His contribution is printed as he wrote it.

In the beginning I was not a Pioneer but Royal Artillery, but I didn't get on very well in there and was always in trouble and on the peg, see, and after I done my last twenty-eight days in the glass-house the battery officer says to me, 'You are crummy and I am going to send you to a crummy mob,' so I come to a Pioneer company and the major was a old sweat like me what I liked and when I come to the orderly room the S.M. marches me in to the old man—which is the way we calls the Major—who is looking at my crime sheets and he says 'This is a b—— poor show, my lad, and being a old soldier you did ought to know better.' So I says, 'Yes, sir,' and he says to remember I am no longer in the Royal Artillery but back in the real army, and so help me God if I play any monkey tricks he will break my b—— heart so that I go to bed and cry myself to sleep at nights, but he will forget my old crime sheets if I don't remind him of them and I says 'Yes, sir' again and thinks to myself watch your step, Ed., becos this old b—— means what he is saying and this is the sort of officer like what you had in the first war and

proper b——s they was, but real officers. So when I am outside I says
to the S.M. 'What is the old man like, Sergeant Major?' and he says,
'Stand to attention when you speak to me, you gutter sweepins, and
say "sir," ' so I stands to attention and says 'sir' like what he said, but
I thinks they are a b—— hot crowd and I am not going to like it very
much.

There were some other blokes what come from other regiments with
bad records like me. This S.M. tells us all, 'Now, you men, let me tell
you something,' and he looks at our papers what he has in his hand,
'You have come from the guards and the tanks and the gunners and
some lousy infantry mobs and they could not handle you and they
sends you to us and now by God you will start proper soldiering and
if you put one foot wrong you will wish you had never been born,'
and that's the way it was. The officers and non-coms was nearly all
old sweats and knew all the tricks and you could not get away with
things like other regiments, and some of the blokes try to play the
old soldier but it does not come off and some of the blokes desert and
the S.M. laughs and says, 'I hope they come back so I can tear their
hearts out,' but they do not come back and some of us stop in the
company and I was one of them and I done very well in the Pioneers
and after I done a year on drills and work I was put in the sergeants
mess as an orderly and so they send us to North Africa and I got a
job as batman and was promoted to officers mess.

When I was in an officers mess I met all the brigadiers and colonels
and General Friend, too, and at the beginning I was windy of them
but afterwards I was not windy any more, because when you have seen
them with no uniform on and only in their little short shirt with their
teeth in a cup you know they are not so big like they make out but
are just ordinary men like us.

We have not been long in North Africa and the Coy. is in a little
town call Bougie and the major sends me to a D.A.D.L. what works
with the arabs. Until I come, the Sgt. and the S.M. cleans up
their own rooms what is a flat where the civvies have gone away and
left when the war come to Africa. Well this is a cushy job and right
up my street as I do not have any parades but being a old soldier I
did not let on but says I have got too much to do and tells the Sgts. why
do you not get one of these arab kids what is always hanging about to
do the dirty work like washing the floors and cleaning out the warehouse, so they say this is a good ideer and we picks out a bright little
kid about six years old what we calls Charlie.

When he first come to us he don't have no clothes only a sack with holes in it, what he puts his head and arms in. Well the Sgts. would not stand for that so they got a old battle dress jacket and trouser and cut them down for him and give him a pair of boots and when he got these on it was a fair treat to see him standing outside the billet with all the arab kids hanging around just looking at him, not saying nothink but just staring with their eyes nearly poppin out of their blinking little heads and young Charlie not taking no notice of them as if he never saw them, but all the time he was fit to bust with pride only he could not wear the boots so he carry them under his arm becos he had never worn boots before in his life and they hurt his feet.

He never took his new clothes home but left them in a corner of the warehouse and change in the morning and again at night when he finish work. When he come in the morning I made him wash his self every time and he got quite clean in the end. Well when young Charlie had been with us for a few weeks it come time for one of the wog feast days what they call the Mutton Feast but we never knew nothink about it becos we have not been very long in wog land so we asks Charlie what it is all about and it seem it is some sort of relidjus feast when they kill a sheep and eat it. The Sgt. asks Charlie is his family going to kill a sheep but he says no becos his father has not any money but a lot of children and it is only the rich arabs what can buy a whole sheep so when he is gone home the 6 of us, the S.M., the 4 Sgts. and me has a talk about it and says it is a b—— shame that Charlie can't have no mutton feast becos he is a good little kid and we all put 100 francs each in the kitty to buy a sheep for him.

The day before the feast day comes the sgts. say as I have to go to the arab market as I am a good scrowndger and buy the sheep which I does. They is all a bit thin looking but I get one which is not so bad. The wog what I buys the sheep from give me a bit of string to tie around its neck to take it back to the billet what is the other end of the town and I sets off with the sheep bleeting at every step and all the wogs laffing and shouting out things what I do not understand. But when I gets out of the arab market it is much worse becos their is a lot of troops about and they starts taking the micky out of me and shouting out 'Baa' so what with them shouting out 'BAA' and with the bleeding sheep going 'Baa' I am nearly drove crazy and then the next thing what happens two red caps come up to me and say, 'Now then who do you think you are—Mary taking her little lamb to school? Where did you pinch that sheep,' and I says, 'I have not stole the sheep I just bought it from a wog.'

Then they arsk me what do you want a sheep for and I do not know if it is wrong to buy a sheep for a arab so I do not tell them but just says I wanted it so they say come along with us and I am marched through the streets by these two red caps still leading the sheep what is making more noise than ever and the troops is laffin to kill their selfs.   In the police offis I am took before an officer and told I have to explain everything so I tells him the truth that I have bought it for Charlie and he tells the red caps, 'Take him back to the market and find the man he bought it off and check that he paid for it.'   So I says, 'Can I leave the sheep here till we get back,' and he say, 'No I do not want that b—— animal making that b—— noise in my offis,' so back we goes to the market, me and the red caps and the sheep, and the

troops in the street is very much amused but I am not and the red caps is not and the sheep does not seem very happy either.

Well the wog tells the red caps that I bought the sheep proper and we go back to the police offis and the officer tells me to get to hell out of it, which I am very glad to do becos now I am very tired of this sheep. So off I goes to the billet but have not got there before a jeep pulls up with some more red caps in

it what says, 'What are you doing with that b—— sheep?' and the next thing I knows me and the sheep is in the jeep and going back to the police offis again.   When I comes up before the officer the second time he is very angry and says, 'O God, not you and your b—— sheep again,' and I says 'Yes sir,' and he says, 'Take him and that blasted animal out of my sight and don't let me never see them again,' so they puts me out in the street and I says to the red cap Sgt., 'Ain't you going to take me back in the jeep to where you picked me up' and he says, 'No, start walking, it's good exercise for you' so again I start to walk back to the billet and it is a long way and I am very tired as it is so hot and the sheep does not like to hurry and I do not think it is a very strong sheep and am afraid it will die on me any minute and then I will have to carry it only it would not make so much noise that way.

Well in the end I get it back to the billet and do not meet no more red caps and we puts the sheep in the yard until the end of the day when the Sgt. give it to Charlie as a present and he stares at it and can't hardly believe it is true and he sniffs a bit like he is going to cry becos he is only a little boy what has never had a sheep before. Then he laffs and hurrys away pulling the sheep behind him so I am afraid he will pull its blooming head orf, and I am very glad to see that sheep go away, as I think now I do not like sheep very much.

But that is not the end of the sheep, for the next day what is the feast day and a holiday for the arabs Charlie comes back with the sheep and a lot more wogs what he says is his father and brothers and uncles and God knows what and they all say thank me very much in wog talk. Now it seems there is a proper drill about killing this sheep and becos we give it to them they has to do the drill in front of us and with that they gets hold of the poor animal and lies it down in the gutter and cuts its throat and lets the blood run away after they have all dipped their hands in it and you never saw such a mess with blood on the pavement and blood on the road and they had blood all over them until I am nearly sick and goes back in to the billet and then they takes the sheep away and we all says, 'Thank God that's done, and we won't buy no sheep for no arab no more.'

But the worst was yet to come as that evening back comes Charlie with his father and his brothers and all of them and they is carrying a tin what has somethink in it with a horrible stink and they tells the Sgt. this is part of the sheep what Charlie's mother has cooked special for us and we have got to eat it. Well, for a long time we do not want to eat this horrible stew but the arabs thinks we is only being polite when we say no thank you and they keeps on saying how good it is and it is for us to eat and they all look so pleased that we do not like to hurt their feelings so we got our spoons and starts to eat this stuff what is worse than it smells so we think they must have forgot to clean the carcass first and we can't eat much but the arabs is quite satisfide and go away.

I am very sorry I write so much only I can't tell the story no shorter. And now I will tell you about the Brigadier and the Colonels goat. It's when I am in Italy and I am batman to a Group Commander what is a very nice man too. An Eyetie what he knowed give him a baby goat for to eat. It was still alive and has only just left its mother. It is a very pretty little thing what the officers do not like to eat. So they makes a pet of it and calls it Wilfred and the Colonel became very fond of Wilfred what always follows him about the house. So the colonel says to me, 'You will look after Wilfred and groom him proper like a horse so he do not stink too much. And don't let no ruddy Eyetie pinch him.' I do like I am told and soon he is quite at home all over Headquarters which is a big private house. He follows me and the colonel around just like he was a dog and everybody make a great fuss of him.

Well, things goes along like this for quite a time. Then when Wilfred has growed up a bit, something goes wrong with his temper and he is not so friendly with everyone like when he was small. Only with me and the Colonel is he still friendly, but with everybody else he is just as likely as not to put his head down and charge at them. No body dont go out without first looking to see is that goat anywhere near. But worst of all Wilfred began to smell, only we never knew in the beginning it was Wilfred. It never come on until the hot summer and everybody starts a sniffin and a turning of their noses up. Some says it was the drains and some say a German soldier has been killed and buried under the floor. Some says it is just the natural smell of Eyetie houses  in the hot weather but in the end you couldn't make no mistake what it was because that smell hung all round Wilfred. It was just like he wore it. Very powerful it was and the other officers wants the Colonel to get rid of Wilfred because he upsets their stummicks. For a long time he will not but then in the end he says to me, 'That there Wilfred do stink horrid bad dont he, take him outside the house and never let him come in no more,' he says. But that is easier said than done because Wilfred has lived in the Mess since he was a few days old and now he cannot understand why he cant go in no more. And this is where my trouble starts because everybody act like it is my goat, which it is not. Every time Wilfred gets away from where he is tied up he comes straight back to the house and it is me what gets blamed for it. It don't matter what I do that blasted goat always escapes. If I locks him up in a shed some b.f. always opens the door and he gets out. So in the end I find a long chain what I tie him up with to a post at the end of the garden. And that is when the Brigadier comes.

When the Colonel hears that the Brig. is coming he gives orders for everything to be spit and span. He says to me, 'You will look after the Brigadier as well as me when he is here and he will sleep in my room. Keep an eye on that b—— goat and if the Brigadier so much as sets eyes on Wilfred I will send you back to a company so help me.'

Well the day the Brigadier comes I have so much work to do in the Mess that I do not have time to think about Wilfred until he starts bleeting loud enough to wake the dead. So I goes down to where he is tied up and he has got his self all wrapped around the post and has nearly strangled his self. Well I undoes the chain and quick as a wink that bleeding goat races away with about twenty foot of chain a rattling and a banging. I chases him all over the garden and just as he heads for the front of the house, I grabs hold of the chain but Wilfred gives a extra hard tug and I slips on the gravel. Down I comes tip over elbow. Blimey what a panic. There is me lying on the ground holding on to the chain and at the other end of the chain is Wilfred with his head down trying to reach the Brigadier what is inspecting a guard of honour of black Basutos. Every now and then Wilfred gives a jump at the Brigadier but because I am still holding the other end of the chain he cannot quite reach him. Every time Wilfred jump the Brigadier jump and every time I try to get up on my feet Wilfred gives another jump and I ends up on my kisser again. Well them black Basutos was standing proper to attention at first but then one laughs and then another one. In a minute they is all stamping and rolling about and slapping each other and double up with laughing. The colonel is yelling and the Sgt. of the guard is yelling. Wilfred is jumping to get at the Brigadier and every time the Brigadier, what is getting a bit pot-bellied, gives a little hop in the air them black Basutos hollers and cheers and laughs. The Brigadier is getting as mad as hell. 'What is the meaning of all this,' he says in the end, 'and who is this man,' looking at me, 'whats it all about?' So I picks up my titfer what I lost and rub some of the dirt and blood off my nose and chin and stands to attention.

The Colonel he dont know what to say so I says, 'It is a goat sir.' 'I can see it is a b—— goat,' says the Brigadier 'do you think I am b—— well blind. Who does it belong to?' he says. He turns to the Colonel, 'Is this a pet?' he asks. 'You know there is orders against keeping pets,' then he sniffs once or twice and says, 'O God, nobody wouldn't keep nothing what smells like that for a pet. Whose is it?'

he says. 'It belongs to an Eyetalian,' I says, 'and is called Wilfred, the goat not the Eyetalian, and I see it in the garden and was driving it out' I says. 'Take the damn thing away' he says. Then he looks at the guard of black Basutos what is now standing proper at the present again and says, sharp like, 'take them away as well.'

Well the Colonel was raving mad and dident half give me a basinful but he quiets down after a bit. He dont say no more about it only to see Wilfred dont get loose no more.

The next day the Brigadier and the Colonel is away all day inspecting companies and things goes off very quiet. In the evening before they got back I lays the Colonel's best uniform out on his bed for to change before dinner. The same with the Brigadier, he having brought a spare uniform with him, also I have got some hot water on so they can have a bath when they comes back.

I pops down to the kitchen for a few minutes and when I goes upstairs again I can smell Wilfred has got loose again and is in the house. I rushes into the Brigs. room and what do you bleeding well think. There is Wilfred standing by the bed a chewing of the medal ribbons what he had pulled off the Brigadiers tunic. I did not know what to do so I give that blasted goat a kick up the backside what lifted it clean in the air. Wilfred lets out one bleet, drops the chewed up ribbon and went out of the house like the devil was after him.

Well them ribbons wasn't no good no more so I takes them to the Lt.-Quartermaster and tells him what has happened and asks him can he let me have some ribbons before the Brigadier gets back. Lucky the other officers has medal ribbons the same as the Brigadier. Also they got spare bits in their kit, and the cook, what was a tailor in civvy street, makes up a posh new set and sews them on the Brigadiers tunic.

He asks me about them after he has had his bath. I tells him as the other ones was looking a bit scruffy I made up a new set for him. He says good man but he could not think of letting me buy new ribbons for him and I must let pay what they cost. So I let him.

He was very pleasant for the rest of his stay and tells the Colonel at dinner on the last day that he has got a very good Headquarters staff. 'I wish I had your cook,' he says to the Colonel, 'this meal is very well cooked and served. What is it?' he says looking at me who is serving at the table. 'Just ordinary rations,' I says. 'There is more flaver to it than anything I get in my mess,' says the Brigadier. Then I sees the Colonel is looking at me a bit strange and not eating so well as he did before. When they goes out to have coffee in the other room the Colonel drops back a bit and comes up to me. 'Was that ordinary ration meat?' he says. 'No sir,' I says, 'its a bit of special what I got.' He says, 'Was it?' and then dont finish what he was going to say. 'Yes sir,' I says, 'Wilfred,' I says. So he goes outside and pukes his heart up. A nice bloke that Colonel was. Pity he had a weak stummick.

Thats the end of that story and heres one about them blokes what come around the Coy. to see how clever you was, with books with little pictures in and all that sort of thing. We had one come round the Coy. when we was stationed in Surrey. The first time he come we was putting on some sort of a concert in the recreation room I forget what it was now and me and another chap was doing a painting job the day before.

The Colonel and a lot of the officers from other Coys. was there having a look round when the Sgt. Major comes in and whispers something to the Major and the Major says to the Colonel 'the trick-cyclist has come, sir, would you like to see him,' and the Colonel says 'Yes.' Now I had not heard that we was going to have a trick-cyclist at the concert so I think I would like to see him as well and stays quiet behind some scenery. The Sgt. Major spots the other bloke what was on this painting job and says 'get out of it you,' but he does not notice me what is behind the scenery.

Well the trick-cyclist come in and he is only a officer and has not got no bike with him at which I was very sorry as I hope he was going to give a rehearsal. He talks to the Major and the Colonel and then brings a lot of papers and things out of a case what he is carrying and all the officers get round a table to see them. From where I am I cannot see none of these papers but I can hear what they is saying and it seems like it is some sort of exam.

This trick-cyclist turns over a page of the book and says to the Colonel, 'this is the sort of thing, sir. Here is six pictures but one of them is out of place, which is it?' And the Colonel looks at it for a minute and says 'dammed if I know,' and some of the Majors looks and some says dammed if they know and some says one thing and some says another and the trick-cyclist says this one and they all say oh, so I think he is not a trick-cyclist after all but one of these blokes what do card tricks and that sort of thing.

Well this bloke shows them some more papers and in the end they all say oh yes they have got the hang of it and the Colonel says, 'what do you do to the men what passes this test?' and the trick-cyclist says we up-grade them into the infantry and the tanks and things like that, so then I rumbles that it is some sort of a game they is going to put over on the lads and this bloke is not a trick-cyclist after all but that is just what they calls him to fool the troops.

I see that our Major and see the other Majors is very angry becos they say it will spoil their Coys. if all their good men is took away so I make up my mind to help our Major and not spoil our Coy. what is a very good one.

When the boys come in from work that evening I gets all our section together and tell them that next week a bloke is coming down from War Office to put a fast one over on us only I make it sound worse nor what it is and says they is going to send blokes what passes this exam into some sort of suicide squad, and in the next day or two we spreads the word round to the other sections.

The next week this officer does not come from War Office but they send some Sgts. instead and every section in turn has to go into the recreation room where we sit down at the tables and this Sgt. tells us they is going to see how clever we are but he do not say nothink about being sent to the infantry if we is too clever so we looks at each other and winks when he is not looking.

So the Sgt. gives each of us a sort of book and tells us to turn to the first page. 'There is six drawings there,' he says, 'but one of them articles has nothink to do with the other ones. All you got to do is put a line thru the one what dont belong. If for instance there is five animals and one bird that bird is out of place and you strike it out or if there is five trees and one flower you make a line thru the flower becos it is different from the others.'

So we goes all thru the papers and blimey I never see nothink so silly in all my life. Even my kids would have done it. You should have seen my paper when I finished—it was a beaut! I nearly died with laffing making up some of the answers.

Well the only blokes what got any answers right was them what was too ignorant to make a mistake on purpose. One day the Sgt. Major comes into the mess and says sarkastic like to the other Sgts. 'you will be happy to learn that we got the most ignorant Coy. in the whole group and the Major is very pleased about it but I dont think it is nothink to be proud of.' 'How's that?' says one of the Sgts. and the Sgt. Major goes on to tell them that we only got three men in the Coy. what passed that there trick-cyclist examination. Some of the other Coys. is losing 30 or 40 men what is being sent to the infantry but we is only losing three.

'B—— blacklegs,' I says. 'Whats that?' says the Sgt. Major, sharp like. 'Nothink,' I says, 'I was only talking to myself,' and then I goes into the kitchen and laffs up my sleeve. But them three men was not much good to the Pioneers anyway. Nice chaps they was, well brought-up like. One of them have been to Oxford and Cambridge and the other two has put in for a comishon, so they wasn't much good for work.

It shows you how dangerous it is to have too much learnin. The Colonel was giving a silver bugle to the best Coy. in the Group for sports and smartness and work and good billets and everythink, but becos we are so scattered up we cannot easy get a football and cricket team together and is afraid we will lose points becos of that, but after the trick-cyclist has been the other clever Coys. lose a bit of their men what was in the cricket and football teams, so when it comes to the competition we are not so bad at sports and walk away with that there bugle as easy as pie.

The Colonel gives us the bugle and a speech at a concert what we have and says what a good Coy. we is and how he is very proud of us and everybody cheers, but I still think they ought to have give me that bleeding trumpet becos if it had not been for me the Coy. would not never have won it. Of course I can not play the trumpet but I bet I could have flogged it to one of them other clever Coys.

*   *   *

Yes, I was there, sir, at the depot last June, I mean. When I got home the Mrs. arsks me have I had a good time so I tells her all about it and she say, 'I bet you will go there again next year Ed.' and I says 'I aint going no more.' The fact is I am only $\frac{1}{2}$ a Pioneer, the $\frac{1}{2}$ what is all right to work in muck and mud and live in a old army hut or a tent and has a dirty old battle dress what he tries to posh up a bit for parades and what swings the led when he gets half a chance.

It is like this, here, sir. I see that depot all clean and shiney, and them boys looking as smart as Guards Men, and the grub all lovely and a proper bed to sleep in and every thing, and I says 'Eddie boy you do not belong to this ruddy army' I says. 'You was all right in the Amps or the Pioneers, but the *Royal* Pioneers is not up your alley.'

If only one Sgt. had hollered at me or one officer had chewed me up it wood not have been so bad, but so help me I sits next to a Colonel at one meal and he was as nice as a lance jack.

And here's a thing. I had been out of the camp to buy some things to take back to the mrs and my 2 girls, and as I comes in past the guard room there is a crash bang wallop and the sentry chucks a salute. 'Blimey,' I says, 'the General must be coming in,' I says, and look a round, but there aint no General or no officers, no body else but me in

me best blue suit with a row of medals on my jacket and the sentry on the verander giving me a butt salute. I got hot all over. I wanted to grin at him and say 'wot cher cock nice morning aint it' but I knowed that was not the proper thing to do, so I put me parsel under the other arm and tips me derby kelly like I seen the officers do, and walks on. Just think of it, me an ex-private retired as you might say taking a salute from the main gate guard of his old regiment.

Believe me, it was not nothink funny, but the sort of thing what makes a bloke feel proud inside but all humble like. Same as when we marches on to the square for that church parade. Just a few old sweats in civvy suits trying to chuck a chest and pretend we was young and smart again like we was about the time of the kaisers war and the medals shining on our jackets and the band up in front playing some think or other. I got a hole in the back of me sock what is rubbing a bit and I am hoping it dont show and there we is on the parade ground with hundreds and hundreds of soldiers all lined up and all of a sudden like they starts a cheering just like the King had come or Chelsea have scored a goal. It was like stopping a kick in the guts. 'What are you sniffing for you silly old basket?' I says to myself, 'swing your bleeding arms' I says 'and march like you was a proper soldier' I says, and all the time I was nearly crying like a kid.

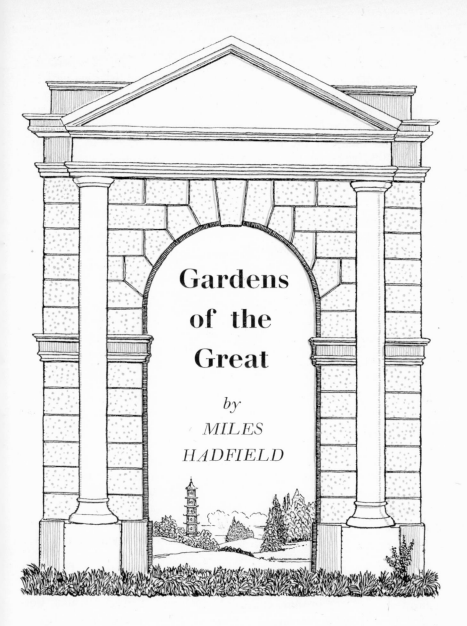

Gardens
of the
Great

by
MILES
HADFIELD

A<small>LTHOUGH</small> we pride ourselves on being a nation of gardeners, our ancient heroes achieved nothing comparable with the potentates of other lands. Not even King Arthur can compete with that 'Nebuchodonosor' who 'magnificently built his hanging gardens' at Babylon. Nor do we learn that King Canute ever tried

I

to emulate that monarch of the much smaller island of Corfu who designed wondrous gardens around which he strolled listening patiently to the long tales told by his visitor Ulysses.

In fact, for a long time our wild and wooded land was not much of a place for gardening. Our own flora were meagre ; most of the plants and many of the trees which we now consider as peculiarly ours—roses, irises, peonies, mulberries, horse-chestnuts—were scarcely known before the restless, searching spirits of the first Elizabethan age collected and cultivated them. The wild forests were perfect for hunting and adventure ; it was not very long since they had been the greatest enemy of man in his attempts to cultivate our land and bring about law and order.

So, in Tudor and even Jacobean days the powerful and great had expressed their grandeur in buildings rather than gardens. These remained small and safely enclosed ; memories of threatening forests were not far away. The little plots were interwoven with paths laid in ingenious geometrical patterns. Coloured gravels were used, and ornaments and nick-nacks were liberally scattered around—a precedent to the china rabbits and concrete gnomes of our own suburbia.

We have little but old woodcuts to show us what these Elizabethan gardens looked like, for, apart from the speed with which nature will destroy man's work, it has always seemed essential to those who follow the latest fashion in gardening that they should obliterate what has recently become outmoded.

Elizabethan extravagance gave way to a more sober style. Sometimes we can gain an impression—it is usually little more—of the appearance of the Jacobean gardens. Obscurity, neglect—even centuries of it—may have left a place comparatively undisturbed by the changes of fashion. Such is Owlpen—but remember, the tall and ancient yews are also suffering from neglect, for they were intended as neat, trimmed little ornaments.

Our story really gets into its stride with the Caroline days. The great then began to spend fortunes on their gardens. Magnificence, European and not insular, came into fashion. Terraced walks, bordered by clipped and trained laurels or boxed orange trees, led to wide flights of stone steps which on descending enticed the visitor to courts where fountains played. Water flowed in canals. Statuary abounded and summer houses were built from which to enjoy the scene. A grotto or two and a wilderness fitted neatly into the plan. One level moved rigidly to another. Outside the walls, avenues (lime

Opposite: OWLPEN
Country Life photograph

'Nature . . . gnarled oaks, whispering aspens, purling streams.'
A view of Hampton Cliffs by Benjamin Barker, from *Landscape
Scenery in and near Bath*, 1824. (J. R. Abbey Collection)

trees were now imported by the thousand) radiated into or cut across the countryside. Man was showing that he was the master.

The style is still seen today on the continent (it reached its climax in the hands of Le Notre), but in our country succeeding generations demolished most of these gardens and replaced them in accordance with later fashions.

Here and there we can see something of their remains, as at Hampton Court. But, fortunately, it was the fashion to employ artists to record these great houses and gardens, and many fine engravings were made of their pictures. Today, when we look at those houses, in settings that would horrify their builders, we can with the help of the old prints restore in our mind's eye the walls and terraces, and walk along the formal avenues until we suddenly encounter the informal banks and bosky hills of the countryside. Or, with pen and ink, we can reconstruct the scene as I have done below.

Architects with their rulers and shears dominated the gardens of the

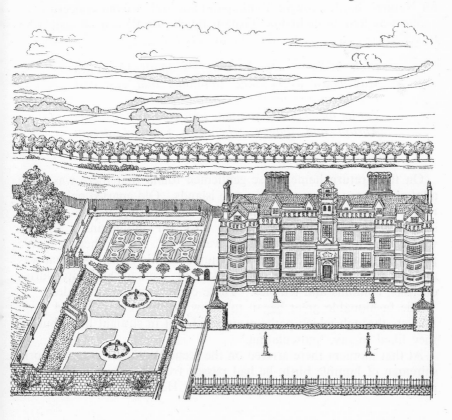

great until Queen Anne's reign. But even before her death, a few persons of consequence were saying the most outrageous things. Addison, for example, not only designed his Warwickshire garden 'as a natural wilderness' but repeatedly praised the irregular in design— though he excused himself as 'an humourist in gardening.' Pope was soon writing of his grootto:

> . . . where Thames translucent wave
> Shines a broad mirrour through the shadowy cave,
> When lingering drops from minerall roofs distill
> And pointed crystalls break the sparkling rill. . . .

No rigid canals, no formal walls there. In short, we were nearing those two inventions of Georgian England whose histories so closely intertwine, Nature and Freedom.

This is not the place to follow the rather lurid history of Freedom, for Nature's battles, fought in ink, paint and soil, are our concern.

She was first brought into fashion by the gentlemen of taste who travelled beyond Paris down to the Mediterranean:

> Rich in her weeping country's spoils Versailles
> May boast a thousand fountains that can cast
> The tortur'd waters to the distant heav'ns;
> Yet let me choose some pine-topt precipice
> Abrupt and shaggy, whence a foaming stream
> Like Arno roars. . . .

On their return home, these gentlemen found that there was quite a lot of Nature to be seen in our own islands. Old gnarled oak trees— relics of our once frightening forests—whispering aspens, purling streams; distant hills that would pass for mountains. Solitary wandering figures at eventide were not unlike hermits. We possessed, too, quite a number of genuine Gothic ruins. All that was missing was the remains of Greek and Roman antiquity—urns, obelisks, columns and temples. These could easily be provided.

The fashionable great began to throw down their walls and plant thickets through which paths meandered, not in straight lines, but, as they liked to say, 'inosculating.'

At that moment there arrived on the scene William Kent. A Yorkshireman of humble birth, he had passed from being an unsuccessful painter to a more successful architect. He grasped the essentials needed to bring Nature to Britain: the park should be brought to the walls of the house, the distant landscape to the park.

Terraces and formality disappeared overnight.   Streamlets were turned into rivers.   Hills were shaved down, banks were raised. Temples and ruins were cleverly set up as 'eye-catchers.'   Thousands of saplings were set, not in avenues, but in clumps and ribbons streaming along the curves of the hills.

Under the dictates of 'Nature,' large tracts of our untidy countryside began to take on the appearance that they have today.

The Yorkshire lad who contrived it all could soon afford to boast of his 'Italian constitution that was unsuited to the English climate.'

But there remained quite a number of the less fashionable great who regarded his innovations as today their successors do the art of Picasso. They came into open revolt when Kent's mantle fell on the shoulders of another self-made landscapist, Launcelot Brown.   Brown banished the last remains of the flower garden and horticulture into secluded corners.   With immense efficiency he laid out estate after estate. Undulating lawns, kept short by teams of mowers, surrounded the square, pillared, classical houses.   The paths that wove around were objects of poetic ecstasy:

Smooth, simple Path! whose undulating line . . .
Plain in its neatness spans my garden round.

Everything, he said, had its 'capabilities'—which gave him a nick-name. For instance (as the poet sang) :

> Some sedgy flat, where the late ripened sheaves
> Stand brown with unblest mildew, 'tis the bed
> On which an ample lake in crystal peace
> Might sleep majestic. . . .

So, with Nature as his motto, ditches became lakes, angular hills that blocked vistas were rounded off ; ancient ragged woods were felled and replaced with saplings lined in tasteful contour—and almost every old garden in the country was obliterated. The English land-scape which, following in Kent's footsteps, he created is only just beginning to disappear.

His vociferous but outnumbered opponents, who believed in the 'picturesque' view of Nature, said that his work resulted in nothing but shaven lawns and :

> Prim gravel walks, through which we winding go,
> In endless serpentines that nothing show :
> Till tir'd, I ask, Why this eternal round?
> And the pert gard'ner says, 'Tis pleasure ground.
> This pleasure ground! astonish'd, I exclaim,
> To me Moorfields as well deserve the name :
> Nay, better ; for in busy scenes at least
> Some odd varieties the eye may feast,
> Something more entertaining still be seen,
> Than red-hot gravel, fring'd with tawdry green.
>
> O waft me hence, to some neglected vale ;
> Where, shelter'd, I may court the western gale ;
> And midst the gloom which native thickets shed,
> Hide from the noon-tide beams my aching head.

The last of our three great landscapists, Humphrey Repton, had a little more sympathy with this point of view. He considered that each garden should be treated in a style according to its own merits. Science was progressing rapidly and a vast number of strange new plants were arriving from overseas. The great wished to outvie each other in cultivating the new and fashionable exotics. Repton therefore had to bring back horticulture ; he gives a design for a range of forcing houses the honour of inclusion in his *Hints on Landscape Gardening*.

Repton was the last of the dictators to work on the grand scale for

SHAVEN LAWNS and a team of mowers. A view of Llanarth, from *The History of Monmouthshire*, illustrated by the Rev. John Gardnor, 1796. (J. R. Abbey Collection)

MR REPTON not only permitted but encouraged forcing houses for winter. Below is reproduced a coloured aquatint from *Fragments on Landscape Gardening*, by Humphrey Repton and J. Adey Repton, 1816 (J. R. Abbey Collection)

The horrors of 'fencing called invisible.' *Above*, an aquatint from Repton's *Fragments on Landscape Gardening*, 1816 (J. R. Abbey Collection). *Below:* Mr and Mrs Benjn. Goldsmid saunter round their Seat at Roehampton. An aquatint from *Seats near London*, by J. Hassell, 1804–5 (J. R. Abbey Collection)

the great; indeed, the great themselves were beginning to disappear. In the gardening magazines of the eighteen-thirties we can notice a significant change. The gardens of the truly great were, of course, indexed separately from those who had merely acquired sufficient money to buy 'a place in the country.' The former appeared under *Seats*, the latter as *Private Residences*. From now on, the entries under *Seats* diminish, while year by year the column of *Private Residences* grows longer and longer. The villa was on its way.

Magnificence was still able to have its fling, though now the absence of fixed standards of taste was leading to a strange confusion of styles. Thus we have the Earl of Shrewsbury's huge fantasy at Alton Towers.

There, among the hills where Staffordshire joins Derbyshire, everything was to be found : an imitation of Stonehenge, a copy of the ever-famous monument of Lysicrates in Athens, not a few genuine ruins and caves, an octagonal Chinese temple—all set among glades planted lavishly with exotic trees and shrubs.

John Claudius Loudon, who took on his shoulders the mantle of Repton, thought Alton a little lacking in taste. He considered that the noble earl who planned it all displayed a certain morbidity of mind. Loudon's own knowledge of plants, particularly trees and shrubs, was encyclopaedic. This was combined with a wide acquaintance with, and a considerable understanding of, the different styles of architecture. His lucid Scotch mind saw the problems of house and garden solved in a relatively simple manner. The increase in knowledge had given us a mass of detailed information of the architecture of the past. The progress in science and the art of construction enabled us to build in any of those styles. Therefore we should build in the style appropriate to the occasion. Thus a baron building a house in some romantic spot should build in the baronial style ; an urban villa at Dulwich should follow an urbane classical model ; while the designer of a lavish country residence for the newly risen plutocrat would naturally seize on Renaissance magnificence as the right means of expression. The gardens were designed to suit, though making full use of the many new plants which horticulturists were importing from abroad and of the numerous devices now being invented for their culture. The idea was simple, logical and practical. Mr. Austin's Artificial Stone, for example, made it possible to produce fountains and other  architectural ornaments in the best taste of all styles at a price undreamed of before. By studying Loudon's publications (he was a great editor and journalist) the new wealthy classes now replacing the ancient great could avoid *gaffes* such as mingling the Gothic and Classic styles. There were other improvements, too. The mowing machine arrived to cut even greater expanses of grass lawn—the picturesque and expensive team of mowers, with the dog to carry the rake, was no longer necessary.

Glasshouses became stupendous. Sir Joseph Paxton, Loudon's rival and, before long, successor, built at Chatsworth the biggest one on record. Coloured engravings of the strange new plants rather than of the gardens in which they were grown became the vogue. Many of these exotics left their greenhouses in the summer and were 'bedded out' to produce riots of bizarre colour. They were rather incongruously planted in trim geometrical patterns.

A strange style of architecture swept the country. Its first symptoms had appeared in isolated spots during Georgian days but now it spread like some violently contagious rash. At the time romantically believed to be Gothic, it was, in fact, purely Victorian. It matched well with the spiked and whorled branching of the new conifers that the eighteen-fifties brought from the American continent. These evergreens altered our scenery quite as much as the earlier work of the old landscape gardeners. Not only the new gardens but the old were within a few years transformed by their dense sombre columns and drooping limbs—for they grew at a speed undreamed of by the Georgians, who had planted mostly our own native trees.

Once again, a Queen ruled over an era of enthusiastic, gorgeous and often tasteless riot of extravagance in gardening—even coloured gravels returned to the paths to be joined by other crushed stones such as Derbyshire spar and 'Blue John' fluor spar, which resulted in glittering stretches of white and purple. Perhaps all this was to counterbalance the sober dress and morals of the day, though there were always dark alleys among the evergreens to remind man of his gloomy mortality.

Nature was now banished to the closets of the naturalists. In increasing numbers they pressed and dried her, named, numbered, and cut her into sections. They almost forgot that she was a living thing. But not for very long. In the eighteen-seventies was heard the voice of William Robinson. As a young working gardener in Ireland he conceived a strong distaste for the fashionable Victorian style. Finally, it became so strong that he let the fires out in his employer's green-

houses, and, having ensured that the choice contents were destroyed, decamped. Soon after making this defiant gesture he arrived in England and set about bringing Nature back to the garden.

In her new incarnation she differed greatly from the version as presented by Kent, Brown and Repton. She still hated formality—bedding out in particular—and iron fences :

'It is not only the tradesman emerging from the city who imagines there is no fence so perfect as an iron one. . . . I regret to see the plague of iron fencing in some of the finest country places . . . no fence is so good as a live one on a bank.'

Now Nature delighted in flowers. The shaven lawn as an ideal was replaced by a vision of 'the winter aconite flowering in a grove of trees in February . . . the blue lupine dyeing an islet with its purple

Opposite: BODNANT
Country Life photograph

PAVILLION & GREEN HOUSE FOR A GOTHIC MANSION.

GOTHIC AND GARDENESQUE
Coloured aquatint from Humphrey Repton's
Observations on the Theory and Practice of Landscape Gardening, 1803
(J. R. Abbey Collection)

on a Scottish river . . . the Appenine anemone staining an English wood blue. . . .'

Robinson was an experienced practical gardener. He was also a skilled journalist. His new Nature doctrine was practical and effectively preached. He was helped, too, by the arrival of a host of plants, particularly gay trees and shrubs such as rhododendrons, which, unlike so many of the earlier introductions, came from temperate regions and would not only prosper in our climate with very little attention but also increase in stature and beauty year by year.

It is to his teaching that we principally owe the landscape gardens that have come to maturity in our own time. Brilliant in colour, subtle in texture of foliage and variety of form, they lie happily and seemingly naturally in our countryside—whether already landscaped by his predecessors or still untouched. Sometimes their scale is vast, as we find in the most famous of them all, Bodnant. Here the very mountains of Snowdonia are brought distantly into the spectacle made by great sweeps of planting with material from all over the world. It all forms an amazing panorama, yet one within the definition of the perfect landscape given by a Georgian connoisseur, one that accords so well with our native dislike of extravagance :

> *The lake or river should be so wide,*
> *As not to show distinctly either side ;*
> *Unless remote, in hazy distance seen,*
> *It dimly glitters through the azure scene ;*
> *Nor should the mountain lift so high its head,*
> *Or its circumference so widely spread,*
> *As each approaching object to o'erfrown. . . .*

Robinson was joined in his campaign by Miss Gertrude Jekyll. She was, as befits a woman, more of a miniaturist. A wise gardener of delicate taste and sensibility, her influence brought about a much more discriminating use of colour in the garden. She is popularly remembered in connection with the development of the herbaceous border, but possibly her most lasting influence lay in her insistence on the need for careful selection from the vast quantity of planting material available and ensuring that the chosen plants were appropriately placed.

'Now that there is so much to choose from,' she wrote, 'we should not let any mental slothfulness stand in the way of thinking and watching and comparing, so as to arrive at a just appreciation of the merits and uses of all our garden plants. . . . There is no spot of ground,

however arid, bare, or ugly, that cannot be tamed into such a state as may give an impression of beauty and delight . . . there is no place under natural conditions that cannot be graced with an adornment of suitable vegetation.'

Miss Jekyll, like Robinson, at first disliked formality and architectural features in the garden. But then she met and worked with the last of the great architects, Sir Edwin Lutyens. His extraordinary genius laid out the skeleton of the garden which was to be covered with a fabric that she wove, formed into a garment which gradually spread out until its edges merged gently into the countryside.

So it came about that in the last of the gardens designed for the great the formality of fine architecture was joined with a new view of Nature. For the last time beautiful fountains fashioned from lovely materials—no more of Mr. Austin's Artificial Stone—cast their reflections in still waters, their spray drifting over the flowers.

But in this perfection was the end, too—for now the great were no longer rich enough to have magnificent gardens. Even during the nineteenth century many of their estates were enveloped by the growing towns. Public-spirited citizens, often fighting against opposition, sometimes managed to acquire a small part to be kept as a public park. Asphalt now replaces William Kent's gravel. A bandstand rears its cast-iron columns under the tulip tree that Pitt admired. A blue vitreous-enamelled sign reading *Gentlemen* points to the sequestered grove of which the poet Shenstone sang. But something still remains.

Even councillors and corporations have difficulty in obliterating their contours and enucleating the now massive—if lopped—trees, let alone exorcising the gentle ghosts whose shadows persistently haunt their ancient walks.

Other gardens, but, alas, not many, have had a happier fate. The National Trust has them in its care.

But even so, we must feel a little uneasy over their future. No garden was ever brought into being by an Official Organization. They were formed by individuals and maintained down the centuries by the personal devotion of their successors. Buildings can be kept in perfect order, century after century, by architects and builders following the rules and traditions of their craft. But what rules are to be followed at Hidcot or Bodnant or Winkworth when the  genius of their creators has left the scene and momentous decisions on felling and replanting have to be taken?

Here and there you will find an old house lingering on in its landscape. The trees around it are now aged and as their planters dreamed of them. The ruin on the island in the lake is now truly falling down, but serves to harbour the water fowl. You and I will probably be able to follow in the footsteps of the great who once wandered round—but only on Saturday afternoons in summer, when a small charge is made for admission. A great-grandson of the man who brought the scene into being will probably be acting as our guide. He will show us the portraits of his ancestors. The oldest of them will be gazing through the windows at the view that did not exist in their time—perhaps it will change again before long. Others, being great, are almost certainly smiling.

For his seventh successive appearance in these pages we asked Fred Bason, the Collector's Curiosity, to write about one of his first loves, cartophily—or collecting cigarette cards, as lesser mortals know it

Got a Fag Card, Mister?

by FRED BASON

IT'S now over ten years since little boys and girls asked us for cigarette cards. Yet in the 1930s thousands upon thousands of people in all classes were cartophilists. This is the posh word for collectors of cards. It comes from the Greek *khartes philos*—a lover of cards, or rather, in this case, papyri leaves. Stamp-collectors get hoity-toity over Philately ; so we have Cartophily. Fair's fair. Today there are still several thousand keen collectors, but with no new stock the numbers diminish each year.

Early in 1938 I wrote the very first book on this hobby. It was called *The Cigarette Card Collector's Handbook and Guide*. It was published at one shilling. It is now a collector's item, and I only possess one copy (not for sale). I started the hobby in 1920, when an uncle gave me 500 cards of various series that he'd collected in World War One. When World War Two began I owned 2,000,000 cards. Today I doubt if I have 50,000. In less than four minutes in 1940 one of Hitler's fire bombs made a huge gap in my collection. As the flames went up my passion for the hobby burnt itself out with them. From that day onwards I never purchased another card.

Perhaps you don't realize that cards have been in existence since 1880. I doubt if anyone will really know for sure how many sets were issued, for every week fresh discoveries are made. Some sets are still worth sixpence, some six pounds. In the early 1930s I was one of four dealers in cards, and we all had our own staffs, our catalogues, and at least 40,000 collectors to share amongst us.

It started like this. . . . The earliest cigarettes were packed in fragile paper packets. It was noticed after a time that the cigarettes got damaged in transport, so a piece of cardboard was placed inside the packet to stiffen it, and to protect the fags. This was at first a plain piece of pasteboard. In the year 1880 there was a Presidential election in America and a series of four cards of the rival candidates was issued. Where better to put them than into packets of cigarettes, as 'stiffeners'? This was done by a tobacco firm named Thomas

Above: one of a rare English set, 'Gallery of Beauty' (50), and 'Famous Authors and Poets' (25).

On the far *right* and *below:* American series of 'Beauties,' *c.* 1898.

Near right: a rare and early French card.

Above: one of the 12 recruiting cards and one of the 'Women on War Work' issued in the first World War.

Right: a very rare and early American card,

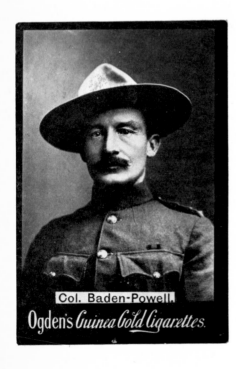

H. Hall. So began the hobby of cartophily. In 1882 another firm named James issued a series of cards with a little coloured boy holding tobacco leaves, and, at the base, 'James Crop 1882.' The boy's trousers had a different colour on each of the set of six cards.

The words 'stiffeners' had from the very earliest times been used in the tobacco trade for cards, and still is.

Mark you, the idea of picture cards was new only to cigarettes in 1880, for they had been packed with trade commodities like soap, coffee, and patent medicines before them. Trade cards are quite another hobby, and a nice one. Another firm worth a mention is Kinney, which was famous for its pretty girl cards. But it was Duke's who started the real vogue when they issued nine albums of reproductions of the complete sets so that the customers could see what the whole series looked like. It was the best of all sales talk. Duke made a fortune. Duke University, endowed with over 78,000,000 dollars, is one of the by-products of cigarette pioneering in America. Amongst the pioneers we must also mention Allen and Ginter, who issued 44 sets, and 25 special albums to put them in, prior to 1891, and many more sets after that date. By 1888 at least seven firms in America were issuing series.

I don't believe there is a man in the whole world who can say with proof and authority which was the first English set. We know that in 1886 Messrs. Wills were issuing trade cards, roughly 156 by 103 millimeters in size. They had views of buildings on one side and adverts for Wills' brands of tobacco on the reverse. They were not stiffeners, but trade cards, as they were all the same and were intended for display on counters. By 1888 other firms were issuing cigarette trade cards in England. Around 1888 Wills issued a series of reproductions of their packet covers—hardly what we call cigarette cards, but much prized today by cartophilists. I have seen an 1888 American card with an advert for an English brand of cigarettes on the back, done with a rubber stamp. Obviously a firm bought cards from America with plain backs and stamped their own advertisement upon them. Ogdens was a pioneer firm for using American cards in this method, and did much around 1900 to make us card-conscious in England. Certain it is, however, Hall, Allen and Ginter, Kinney and Mayor started issuing real fag cards before anyone in Britain.

I think it is as well to record that the first maker of cigarettes in England was a man named Gloag, and he lived and had his firm in Walworth, where the author of this record was born and has lived all

his life.   Perhaps that's why I became a pioneer dealer in cigarette
cards.   But Gloag never issued picture cards with his cigarettes.

Now for a little about the cash values of cards.   I am going to list
a few rare sets that are comparable in the world of cartophily to the
'penny blacks' of the stamp collectors.   In actual cash, in the year
1952, these sets are all worth over three pounds a set, in clean and
sound condition.

Ogden's 'Lady Cricket and Football Teams.'
T. E. Yeoman's 'Beautiful Women.'
Player's 'A Gallery of Beauty' (see illustration).
Player's 'Castles and Abbeys' (20 to a set).
Faulkner's 'Puzzle Cards.'
Murais' 'World's Distinguished Personages' (unknown how
many complete a set).
Taddy's 'Natives of the World.'
Salmon and Gluckstein's 'Heroes of the Transvaal War' (40 to set).
South Wales Tobacco Co.'s 'Views of London' (25 to the set).
Wills' 'Cricketers' (of 1896). The 'Cricketers' of 1901 are
only worth about one pound for a set, but the issue of 1896 would
be a bargain at three pounds a set of 50.
Couden's 'British Beauty Spots' (60 to the set.   In 30 years of
collecting I have never seen or heard of a complete set).
Adkin's 'Soldiers of the Queen.'

One can add, of course, the many sets that were printed in England
for export to China and places Far East around 1905, and, of course,
many dozens of early American cards of the 1888 vintage.   But what
would be the use?   It's unlikely that you have them stored in your
attic, along with the aspidistra.   The sets I have listed above are gems
that cartophilists all over the world want and will buy for good cash.
Personally, I'd rather have those thirteen sets than fifty pounds.   But
there are thousands of modern sets that are only worth from one to
fifty shillings a set in mint condition.

Don't think that only U.S.A. and Britain packed cards.   They were
issued in practically every country—the sauciest from Cuba and
France, the prettiest from America, the most curious in Java.

Every time in the past twenty years I have written articles on cards
for magazines I have been offered hundreds of Ogden's Guinea Gold
and Tab cards.   Now, although they were issued around 1901, there
are still thousands of them about.   But so far as is known there is
only *one* complete set in existence, for you require over 6,000

different cards to make one set. Oddments are merely curiosities, and worth no more than a penny each. But I would say that a set would realize all of a thousand pounds.

In London there are two excellent clubs solely devoted to my hobby; the Cartophilic Society and the Cameric Club. The former meets at Caxton Hall, Westminster, at regular intervals throughout the year, and anyone interested in cards is very welcome. Both clubs hold auction sales where you can buy sets for a few pence or a few pounds. The reason for the few pence is that most of the members of both clubs are advanced collectors and already have the common issues of the 1930 vintage. If you took along a clean set of 16 cards entitled 'The British Royal Family,' which were issued by firms named Charlesworth and Austin, and W. Faulkner, as well as four other firms, you would probably be astounded and delighted at the price they would realize under the hammer. In 1940 I saw a man pay eight pounds for these 16 cards.

We who love cards have had to withstand superior smiles from stamp collectors for many years. Yet you will not find anywhere else such accurate and concise information, in such a small space, and upon every subject under the sun. Just as errors and curiosities creep into stamps and first editions of books, so, of course, do they creep into cigarette cards, causing some extraordinary freak valuations. But when you think of the hundreds of millions of cards that have been printed it is amazing how few cards were printed with incorrect information or the picture wrong in some manner of detail. In collecting for over 30 years I have only discovered 90 error cards.

Probably the most famous card collector of today is King Farouk. He is also the most famous collector of matchbox labels. My last ambition in the world of cards is to exchange cigarette cards of the finest vintage with King Farouk.

I have sold cards to film stars and to dustmen; and to all it's the same price—ten shillings and sixpence for a nice mixed collection of over one hundred, all clean, and all different. I shall never change that price. As I look at my collection I recall some funny little trips I've had. I remember going to Cadiz in a little ship from Casablanca. A man was taking over food and cheap quality shoes, and I've an idea that he took over naughty things like guns as well. The Civil War was on, and the folks were not particularly civil when I went around asking for cigarette cards. They thought I was crackers, or that it was not quite 'the thing' to gather cigarette cards when folks were starving, sweating and dying. But it was not my blooming war, and I was offer-

K

ing good, high, and clean money for cards. In the four days I got about 250 genuine Spanish cards. Also I nearly got my little head knocked off for asking Ernest Hemingway if he'd gotta fag card. But I was in earnest.

I am a born collector. I do not for one moment regret it. I have collected practically everything but a wife (and, please, I am *not* in any way a sissy or a freak ; all I am is a little particular. Only five women have come into my life. Two were utter—well, I won't say it! I wrote about one in last year's *Saturday Book*. The other robbed me and gave it to her lover. Another woman got religious mania and is now no use to anyone, not even herself).

Cigarette cards found me the woman who was the one joy of my life up to now. (Save for my very loyal and loving Lizzie, who, in case you are interested, happens to be a grandmother three times over, but has been my faithful landlady for 19 wonderful years.) The 'joy' was a German girl named Nalda. She was five feet seven, with golden hair, blue eyes, strong legs, and able to say 'Yes' and *mean* it.

It so happened that I went over to Germany about two weeks before the war with two purposes in mind. I wanted to swop cards with Hitler, and also invest all my little capital in German cards before our boys went over and bombed both the cards and the cities to ashes. Would they take good English pound notes for good German cards? I got about a thousand. It was by no means enough. It would not cover my fares. I had very soon found how hopeless it was to try to exchange cards with Hitler. Suddenly I recalled a lad called Paul whom I had befriended on the boat going over. He'd given me his card. I sought him out. He was a bank clerk. It was impossible for him to travel through Germany with me as my interpreter, but he introduced me to his sister and he explained what I needed. Bless his human heart! It was all Sir Garnet from the word go.

Had the ruddy war held off, say, six months instead of a few hours when we parted I would have brought her home and married her. We travelled from Hamburg to Berlin, with many stops on the way. She did all the business, and I paid the bills. It was all summer. We were very much in love, and knew it—and cared not who knew it. Her English was not much, but just enough.

I brought back many thousands of top-grade cards from Germany, and the *first* German incendiary bomb that fell in my road fell upon my house and destroyed the lot of them. (And I never got fourpence compensation.) As I saw those cards ruined, my heart went out of the hobby. From that day onwards I never again bought cigarette cards for cash. All that I do now is exchange them for anything collectable. At the moment I am exchanging American novels . . . one good novel for 50 clean cards . . . 20 clean stamps for 30 clean cards . . . don't matter which way round. It all leads to international good will and friendliness. That's the good point about hobbies. You can't do it if you collect blondes.

Yes, I have collected almost everything except a wife. Right at this moment, friends, I estimate that I own 15,000 postage stamps, 11,179 first-class autographs of notable folks, 600 top-grade match-box labels, 400 foreign coins, 3,000 autographed photographs of famous stars of screen, stage and radio ; a lovely collection of rare Christmas cards of the 1880 period, a couple of charming musical boxes, four perfect examples of ships in bottles, 2,000 pretty good books, many of which are autographed by their authors, several dozen odd volumes of the *Saturday Book,* so that anyone who lacks a volume to make their set of 12 complete has but to write to me and he or she gets it . . . at a price. Add to these some faded lilies given personally to me by Pavlova—and her ballet shoes. Add some 40,000 picture postcards, none of them dirty.

Looking at my cigarette cards I can recall high-class suppers with high-class company, paid for by me solely on the proceeds of the sale of a few sets of cards. I was quite a kid when I sent a set of clean cards to Albert, King of the Belgians, in exchange for his auto-graph. (Yes, I had the cheek of the devil even in those young days.) I will not send a set to King Farouk, as I already have his autograph. I swapped it for a signed photo of Jack Dempsey. Another interesting swop I made was the signature of Rouse, who was hung for murder. I mistook him for a famous organist and got it about a year before he committed murder. There is in U.S.A. a man who only collects the autographs of murderers. Well, I did not want such a nasty signa-ture, so I made a swop and got Tosti, who wrote 'Good-bye.'

And now I'd better say 'Good-bye' myself. I've enjoyed going back to my old hobby, and thinking of all the friends it made. Maybe if you added together all the fag cards I've ever had they couldn't buy a Van Dyck or a First Folio. But they've been worth much more to me. I don't envy a soul in the world. I don't want to be anyone else but Yours Sincerely, Fred Bason. I now wear a tidy trilby instead of me old cloth cap, since Fred Bason's Second Diary, edited by L. A. G. Strong, is now published, and I'm told I've 'arrived' (I don't know where). But the address is still the same : 152 Westmoreland Road, Walworth, London, S.E.17.

Champagne in History

by T. A. LAYTON

FROM the days when it was found to have a natural sparkle, until now, when science has got the making down to such a fine art that further improvements can hardly be possible, the history of champagne has been as vibrant as the wine itself.

Long before it was sparkling, and throughout the middle ages, the wines of Champagne had been growing in popularity, but whether it was because the Kings of France were crowned at Reims, or whether it was merely that the wine was better than elsewhere, is unknown. As far back as 1397, when the King of Bohemia arrived to make a treaty with Charles VI, it is recorded that he spun out his errand as long as possible in order to drink the wines of Champagne. Two centuries later a special characteristic of these wines had been noticed; they were called 'cork-jumpers' or 'bedevilled wines.' Why should this happen to the particular wines of Champagne? There were three theories— one, that it was something to do with the phases of the moon; two, that it coincided with the rising of the sap of the vines in the spring-time; three, that it was connected in some way with the chalky soil of the region. The first theory no longer holds good. The second one is scientifically the most likely; but why should it happen with Champagne more than with any other wine? The third theory may be correct but no one as yet knows why.

At this epoch Dom Perignon, Benedictine monk of the Abbey of Hautvillers, comes on the scene. He is usually loosely described as the inventor of champagne; he was nothing of the sort. Nature invented it. What Dom Perignon did ('never was a man more skilful in the production of wine') was to think out the cork as we know it today, and to do away with the old wooden bungs loosely wrapped round with oil-soaked hemp. Although there is now electric bottling, and every modern refinement is used, even down to freezing the small drop of champagne which is expelled from the neck when the second cork is put in the principles which Dom Perignon worked upon have never been modified.

Fifty years later the results of his work had met with remarkable success. But, though vignerons around Reims were turning their hands to producing the sparkling wine we now know as cham-pagne, the still wines were then in almost as great demand. The wines of Bouzy, a commune on the hills outside Reims, were considered by gourmets of the late eighteenth century to have a bouquet approaching that of Burgundy. It was made—and still is—with the *plant doré,* or golden plant, a close relation of the famous Pinot group which Crescenzio, writing in the thirteenth century, called the *pignolus,* and which was even then classed as the finest vine grape of all.

After the French Revolution, which was to make all men equal, the demand that all champagne wines should be sparkling led to a state of affairs in some of the larger merchants' cellars which was almost as tumultuous as, just a century later, it was above ground. It was fortunate that labour was cheap then, because the number of operations to which the wine was subjected was extraordinary. Even today the man-handling of the wine is what makes it expensive. Champagne is the only twice-corked wine in the world. This is done at first in the spring following the vintage. As the wine is far too young to have had time to throw off its sediment in cask, this forms inside the bottle. How then to get these lees out without losing the wine? The answer is this. Each individual bottle is placed, partially upside down, in an individual pigeon-hole. Over the three maturing years, expert workmen shake down the lees on to the first cork. When the wine is sufficiently matured the bottles (now completely upside down) are taken to a freezing chamber where the neck is frozen so solid that about a liqueur glass full of wine freezes with it. Off comes the old cork, out flies the ice bullet, carrying all the sediment with it. To replace the void comes a dosage of wine and brandy (varying in sweetness according to the country of destination); then the new cork, electrically inserted, follows. That in principle was what Dom Perignon did, and they were doing it after the French Revolution.

In 1822 M. Moet's cellars, which then contained a stock of 600,000 bottles (now 2 millions), must have resembled a battlefield. In those days they never tested to see how much unfermented sugar was left in the wine before it was bottled. As the bottles themselves were then made by hand they varied enormously, and it was not easy to tell how they would take the strain. Each one was first carefully scrutinized to see if there were any air bubbles in the glass, then they were again looked over for bottles which had necks which were either a fraction too short or too long. Those that remained were—says a contemporary writer—'jingled together in pairs, or against the others,' and those which cracked or burst were carried in account against the maker. Those that came through this ordeal could be used for bottling the young wine, and this started in April.

If accounts of the time are to be believed, no one had the faintest idea as to how much fermentation would take place. The soil where the vine was grown, the soil in which the cellars were hewn, the depth at which the wine was lying in the cellars, the number of air holes, the types of wine blended, and even the interior surface of the bottles— all these had inexplicable effects upon the in-bottle fermentation of the wine. Sometimes, it was recorded, a current of air would set a bin of the wine fermenting furiously, while another bin of identical wine, bottled on the same day, but put away in another part of the cellar, would be quite flat. Year in, year out, the maker was faced either with the wine being too powerful for the bottles or with wine which had not developed. Odd as it must seem to us today, he preferred losing the wine through too high a breakage rate, to uncorking still bottles and blending it with a fully effervescent succeeding vintage. The breakage rate was stupendous—eight per cent of the wine bottled— compared with today's rate of less than one-half per mille. August was the peak fermentation month, and during this time workmen were obliged to go about in the cellars wearing wicker masks, so forcibly was the glass scattered around. Make no mistake, it really was dangerous, and in M. Moet's cellars during the summer months, 'several dozen bottles were exploded daily, fouling the air and charging it with new principles of fermentation which tends to increase the loss.'

A hundred years later the popping of corks had ceased in the cellars and all was quiet down below. Above, in the town of Reims, a more dangerous popping occurred. After intensive shelling, the Germans entered Reims on September 4th, collected a hundred hostages and a million francs from M. Charles Heidsieck and other champagne merchants as a fine because the town had not supplied sufficient rations for German troops. The Germans were chased out again nine days later. But not far enough for the inhabitants of Reims, who, for the next four years, settled down to an extraordinary troglodyte existence in the vast chalk cellars of the town. Soon, side by side with the routine work of bottling, and the 'remuage' (i.e. the gradual shaking down, as previously described, of the deposit on to the top of the first cork ; the most important single operation in the art of champagne making and a difficult trade to master), a complete civilian underground life got under way. Children thought they were in for a permanent holiday, but they were disappointed. Every above-ground school had been requisitioned by the army, but it was not long before M. Foumann had started classes in nearly every one of the large champagne cellars. There, with their gas masks around their waists, and cheek by jowl with the underground tailor, watch repairer and shoesmith, the young of Reims were educated. Although people soon became acclimatized, it is recorded that 'several of the women did not see the light of day for two years.' Surprisingly, although the air was saturated with humidity, and the smell of petrol cookers and food was frightful, there were no epidemics at all.

The Protestant Chapel was installed in the cellars of Krug, while the Cardinals' altar, surrounded by 100,000 bottles of vintage 1911, was erected in those of Pommery and Greno, and other smaller ones in Roederer and Mumm. Here the faithful came to pray. Here too they came to pilfer great quantities of champagne.

However thirsty the Germans were, nine days can have made little inroad into that vast store compared with four years' systematic thieving by soldier and civilian alike. The military made quite a business of it. When a negro soldier was killed by falling through one of the deep air holes on his way down for his nightly basketful of bottles he received a posthumous medal, though the citation was somewhat vague.

If the many remaining citizens found safety in the champagne cellars, it is impossible to exaggerate their value to the military. 'The stabilization of the frontline of battle around the outskirts of Reims meant that, as a result, the vast underground galleries where champagne merchants had their cellars suddenly became of the greatest though unexpected importance,' writes an official historian of the war. Pommery's cellars were by far the largest and most suitable, and one wonders whether the sudden smart popularity the wine enjoyed in the 'Twenties was due to its famous agent André Simon, or to the hosts of visitors and weary soldiers who found rest there. However that may be, thirty-five yards below ground, 'it was possible to house a battalion and a half, i.e. 1,500 men, together with three-quarters of a mile of benches and sixty latrine buckets.'

In March 1916 the military circulated an official but highly secret memorandum on the potentialities of the champagne cellars, in which it was stated that 34 battalions, nearly 50,000 men, could be housed therein. The memorandum throws an interesting sidelight on to the ups and downs of champagne names. Who, for instance, has heard of Rogeron, Werle, Abele or Chauvet? Yet their cellars offered to take in a total of 4,700 men—as much as Krug, Heidsieck, Roederer and Irroy.

In spite of the pilfering (some champagne merchants complained to the Government about it after the war, and were roundly rebuked for their unpatriotism), champagne had a 'good war,' and this in some measure can be put down to the perseverance and even courage of the vignerons who tended the vines. We said further back that the most important single operation was the remuage. 'Single' was used because in the making of all wines it is the viticulture which counts. Grapes do not just grow ; they have in Europe to be grafted on to American root stocks to prevent attack from a tiny deadly plant louse, the phylloxera. Against the oïdum or mildew frequent sulphuring must take place, an operation which turns the leaves an attractive shimmering blue-yellow colour during the summer months, until the winter rain turns all to green again. And though the finest vines dislike a rich soil, that does not mean that incessant hoeing need not take place.

The champagne vineyards were no exception, but though the men were away, volunteers were found, and the 1914 vintage was gathered, even if under difficulties. Thousands of soldiers were in trenches dug actually in the vineyards from which champagne was made. On both sides there were complaints of the difficulties experienced by the cavalry in traversing the vineyards, which are, of course, trained along stout iron wires. Most remarkable of all, the wine grower Corpart received a decoration for his bravery in bringing in the vintage. Always under bombardment, sometimes under gas attack, and right under the French batteries, this intrepid Frenchman would wait till fog descended or the moon rose to continue his work. In 1916 G.H.Q. gave permission for champagne houses to bring back the gathered grapes into Reims itself, and it says much for men like Corpart and others like him that the 1916 was one of the finest ever, and that twenty-one years had to elapse until 1937 equalled it. From September 1914 to the great evacuation in 1918 no less than 20 million bottles were sent off, one firm contributing on its own no less than 6 million bottles of this total.

The 'great' evacuation, as it was called, took place in March 1918, and was a tragedy. After living for so long in such warlike conditions, the inhabitants were more than loth to leave the personal belongings they had held on to for so long. But the shelling became worse, and everything had to be abandoned, even livestock. An official notice, which could be seen on the walls for many months afterwards, read : *Poultry ; persons leaving the town who possess poultry should go, in order to liquidate them, to the municipal soup kitchens.*

Seven months later the big German retreat started. In the early hours of the morning of October 5, 1918 the last shell fell upon Reims. Champagne, Dom Perignon's elixir, was free to enliven the world again.

ROME

Eight studies by
PETER & RODERICK
PRYOR

ONE of the colossal equestrian
statues of Castor and Pollux
at the top of the Cordonata,
the steps leading up to the Capitol.

THE remaining columns of the Temple of Castor and Pollux, seen from the steps of the Temple of Antoninus and Faustina.

203

T H E Basilica of Constantine,
the first Emperor to become
a Christian.

THE inescapable tetragram, *Senatus Populusque Romanus*— 'the Senate and the Roman people'—will be found throughout the city, on the oldest statuary and the latest mayoral proclamations. *Below:* some of the original stones in the Appian Way.

S OME twenty miles to the east of Rome
lies Tivoli, in the Sabine hills, set
among vineyards and olive trees.

206

IN the terraced gardens of the Villa d'Este at
Tivoli, among extravagant waterfalls, are
some of the world's finest cypress trees.

COLETTE
A legend in her lifetime

Reading anti-clockwise, we see Colette as a child—
her mother's 'golden jewel'; as the young bride of
the egregious Willy; as the author of *Claudine à
l'Ecole*; as a member of the curious threesome
which included the lovely cabaret star, Polaire;
and, suitably decked with bays, as the Grand Old
Lady of French literature today

Colette

by *KAY DICK*

FRANCE honours few women writers, which makes the fame of
Madame Colette even more luminous and remarkable. The
French are proud of Colette, with their connoisseur's pride in
wine, in art, in period furniture : basically prosaic, extrinsically casual,
spiritually impassioned. In France Colette's work is a popular enjoy-
ment, as indispensable to Paris as the Eiffel Tower and the Ile St
Louis. Beyond France, due to indifferent and uninspired translations,
Colette's books have until quite recently been enjoyed only by those
able to read them in the original. Fortunately, Messrs. Secker and
Warburg have decided to issue, under the perceptive editorship of
Mr Raymond Mortimer, new and lively translations of Colette's work.

Love is Colette's theme. The infinite variety of love, of desire, of
sensuality ; the immeasurable joy and immeasurable anguish of love—
such is the compass of Colette's work. And this love, which Colette
describes so exuberantly, disregards all relative conventions and
embraces the thousand and one shapes of love, irrespective of
what is classified as normal sexuality. Love, viewed by the majority
of novelists, is too restricted for Colette's widely selective net.
Deliberately she forces her readers to reconsider the boundaries of
love and the limitless interpretations and realities of the heart and the
body's desire.

Today Colette is seventy-nine, crippled by arthritis and unable to
walk: she sits in a large cushioned invalid's chair at her writing-table
near the long windows overlooking the gardens of the Palais Royal.
These windows are her only view of the world, of Paris, the very heart
of Paris, the country in the centre of Paris. Behind her a collection of
paperweights, some pressed butterflies, an unfinished piece of tapestry :
before her the paraphernalia of her work—the books, the sheets of
writing-paper, the proofs, the small flower-jug holding a variety of
fountain pens—occupational testimonials. 'And even now, after half
a century,' she says, 'I still think I follow the most difficult of trades.'

A short, plump-bodied woman, immediately recognizable by her
wild, frizzy mop of grey hair, like some Toulouse-Lautrec head, a
deliberate physiognomical diversion to keep the stranger at bay, while
the inquisitive nose, the ironically tender mouth and the large tem-
pestuous eyes survey, inspect and note what ultimately the alert,
expressive, busy little hands will write.

A mocking, teasing, shrewd little Frenchwoman looking out at Paris. As much as Paris belongs to Colette so does Colette belong to Paris. Each has the same kind of capriciousness and lightness of heart ; the alert sensibility ; the mercurial intellect, tender, curious and analytical ; the restless melancholy ; and the basic knowledge of the relative cost of pleasure and ' pain.   The city made the woman famous and the woman's work makes the city more memorable ; for in Colette's forty or more books is the wonder and delight of Paris, like a harlequin's ghost beckoning the fair ones and the dispossessed.

It is of these fair ones and these dispossessed that Colette writes. They are fair not because of their deeds nor dispossessed because of their politics : each finds his particular heaven and hell in the simplicity and complicity of love.   And Colette, who creates them, who knows them and is them, is Madame Colette of the Goncourt Academy, respected, revered and honoured as one of the greatest original contemporary French writers.   A master of the art of the intricately insinuating use of prose ; an accomplished and infinitely talented exponent of verbal hypnosis ; a writer intent upon reiterating the same theme with the precision of a highly-skilled technician.

A legend of eccentricity, Colette occupies an unusual position among her fellow writers, most of them are bound to more rigidly traditional and educative inheritances.   Not so Colette, who scandalized conventional opinion in the 1900's because of her marriage to Willy and her music-hall performances.   With such flamboyant beginnings, what English writer (particularly woman writer) could attain such academic renown as Colette?

Structurally Colette is a conscious stylist ; a determined excavator of the adroit word, of the consummate image ; an instinctive perfectionist ever alert to the influence of atmosphere and undertone. Fundamentally Colette is an artist, able to reveal with a sharp impressionable truth the many facets of direct and indirect experience.

A row of titles, what do they tell us?   What album of experience do they unfold?   The author's name attracts attention.   Colette— simply Colette.   Is this mockery?   The English reader is cautious. Colette—just Colette—the casual intimacy is somewhat arrogant.

The *Claudine* novels (when Colette was ghost-writing for Willy, her charming and despotic husband) still reek of a period scandal, faintly perfumed reminders of the preposterous recklessness of early years when youth was ardently curious and rashly defiant.   The aftermath of Willy and the beginning of mature sensuality in *La Retraite Sentimentale* ; the bitter adult fulfilment of *La Vagabonde* and *L'Entrave* set against the uneasy febrile atmosphere of music-hall dressing-rooms and grease paint. The popular success, *Chéri* and *La fin de Chéri*— immaculate and wanton love of the gigolo for the high-class courtesan, raised from the commonplace to the realm of perfection because of the author's infinite compassion and ability to create the individual Chéri among so many Chéris. And *Gigi* (Chéri's feminine counterpart) irrepressibly delicious and outrageous ; and Minne of *L'Ingénue Libertine,* biologically amoral and continuously desirable.

A taste is acquired ; the taste becomes a thirst for the rich, warm-blooded wonder of this writer to whom life is so unashamedly love, with the gaiety and the disaster of its circumstances.

Volume after volume proclaims this allegiance to love, although as the years pass the setting becomes less personal, and love is viewed more as the experience of others, such as *Le Blé En Herbe, La Chambre d'Hotel,* and *Julie de Carneilhan.*

Then come the autobiographical volumes, curiously incomplete yet wholly satisfying. The cynical *Mes Apprentissages,* sub-titled *'What Claudine could not say,'* a wicked and devastatingly revealing record of Colette's life with Willy ; fiercely partisan, tantalizingly oblivious of omission, the female cad at work manipulating the rapier Willy had taught her to use—the pen. Elusive and disturbing are the miscellaneous journals, the memoirs, the later reflections, *L'Etoile Vesper* and *Le Fanal Blue,* with their flavour of lost pleasure, lost because now the body is cramped by age and the remembering mind can only partly savour life that goes on and on. 'When ill-fortune prevails we must accept and know how to fashion it to our needs.'

And Colette? What of Colette behind this row of titles? There she is in her books, distributing her varied selves in the precocious experimentalism of *Claudine* ; in the watchful narrator of *La Retraite Sentimentale,* in Renée of *La Vagabonde* and *L'Entrave,* and in *Chéri* too, she is there. Impossible to locate precisely, Colette is narrator, heroine, hero, incidental character and unintentional spectator.

Yet facts do inform, and Colette's life, shown through her work and the reminiscences of others, is clotted with facts. At times the chronology is diffuse, maddeningly non-committal.

The basic lines are deceptively simple. Sidonie Gabrielle Colette was born in 1873 at St-Saveur-en-Puisaye, wine-growing Burgundy country. Innocent early years of rural calm ; local schooling, sheltered within the security of a loving and happy family circle. Colette was her mother's youngest and favourite, mother's 'golden jewel.' A watchful, observant and remembering child who immortalized her mother in a tender, teasing book, *Sido*. 'Sido,' Colette's mother, was a quick-witted Belgian housewife, contemptuous and yet envious of Parisian frivolities, who philosophized as she busied herself about the house and garden. The original manuscript of *Sido* is bound with material from one of 'Sido's' blue skirts—symbol of nineteen years of great devotion. Brought up among painters, journalists and musicians, 'Sido' was proud that her contact with *la vie de Bohème* had not shaken her obstinate worship of the bourgeois conventions : at all times Colette kept from 'Sido' the darker aspects of her marriage with Willy. Colette's father, a retired sea captain, large, handsome and a magnificent story-teller, bore with equanimity 'Sido's' persistent scoldings— 'Sido's' way of proclaiming her ferocious loyalty. It was 'Sido' who, during Colette's first years of marriage, arrived in Paris like a battling missionary, to sniff about Willy's apartment, and who expressed contempt of her son-in-law's earning capacity by taking her daughter out and buying her a winter coat. It was 'Sido' who nursed Colette through a long winter illness, sleeping in the dining-room and refusing directly and indirectly to address her son-in-law other than as 'Monsieur Willy.'

No record tells what attracted or brought Willy like a hurricane into Colette's rural peace ; he came like the country's mistral, precipitously, to raise the devil and to marry the young Colette.

She was nineteen and Willy was fifteen years older. A tall, fat, extravagantly-bearded charmer from the city, with a golden voice, selling the secrets of life as unconcernedly as a gipsy. Colette's marriage to him was a private and public adventure : mercilessly educative to the young country girl whose robust temperament enabled her to turn the disadvantages to a personal triumph.

Willy, Henry Gauthier-Villars, boasted that cannon and church bells sounded at his birth : on this day, the 15th of August, 1859, the Treaty of Villa Franca was signed ending war between France and Italy. He spoke lovingly about his *'archiviste-paleographe'* soul, and fancied himself as a German scholar. When Colette met him he was a celebrated columnist, theatre critic and the author of many scandalous novels. Willy, prolific author that he was, hardly wrote a line : he employed his gifted friends to execute the novels which bore his name (Marcel Boulestin was one of Willy's ghost writers). Willy could sell any work, knew what was good, and by bullying, flattering, cajoling, badgering, made sure that book succeeded book. Into Willy's chain of ghost-writers came Colette. Libelled, slandered, the subject of virulent gossip, Willy is a curious hero in the Colette story. Carelessly

promiscuous, brutal, generous, petty, stimulating, erratic, shocking—
Willy was all this and more, and yet, Colette says, Willy knew, Willy
had a nose for writers. 'An amusing though dangerous person. He
had taste, wit, charm and erudition,' admits Colette. Often Colette
was locked in her room until another chapter was ready for Willy to
sub-edit and publish under his name. And when the book was finished
Willy sold it to the highest bidder. Colette was Willy's showpiece,
paraded about town, dressed to represent the original Claudine ; sober
citizens viewed her as a menace to public morality.

Colette's hey-day was Paris of the 1900's when Sarah Bernhardt
played in *L'Aiglon* and Oscar Wilde was an aged and tired attraction.
Paris of Maxim's, of Zola and the Dreyfus Case, when electricity was
a novelty, and a Cézanne painting could be bought for 300 francs.
Colette, to suit Willy's publicity stunt, had her hair cut short,
dressed in men's clothes and greeted her visitors in the gymnasium
where she and Marcel Boulestin vaulted and swung from a trapeze.
With Willy and the notorious cabaret star, Polaire, Colette appeared
at the small Theatre Royal (now the back room of Weber's brasserie)
where Sacha Guitry made his début. Parisian tongues wagged about
the Willy–Polaire–Colette ménage.

Polaire, known as the woman with the smallest waist and the largest
pearls in Paris, played *Claudine,* dramatized by Willy. Colette described Polaire's short, auburn, curly hair, her large, haunted, long-
lashed eyes, her violently painted red lips, a striking contrast to the
white face, her repetitive 'oh how I suffer!' and her passion for the
theatre. Polaire, said Colette, really created Claudine, and Willy
sold Claudine. Postcards, portraits, caricatures, scenes in revue,
Claudine collars, Claudine frocks, Claudine pornography—all this was
part of Willy's continuous publicity for *Claudine.* Polaire, first discovered and first loved by Willy, was more loved, perhaps, by Colette.

These thirteen years of life with Willy might almost be called the
Claudine years. Indivisible were Claudine's creator, Claudine's
impersonator and Claudine's impressario : a high-powered music-hall
act of Willy, Polaire and Colette ; private lives indistinguishable from
public exhibitions.

Doubtless it was Colette's rigid early training under 'Sido' that
stopped her leaving Willy when, after a year of apparent domestic
felicity, she discovered Willy's inbred promiscuity and conjugal
infidelity. Colette, shocked at first, decided to stay on : economically
she was dependent and there was, too, her disinclination to admit
failure to 'Sido.' Moreover, Willy had something which Colette

needed, and which she intended to acquire and to use every bit of—life. Could she then have abandoned Willy, since leaving Willy meant leaving behind all that strange intoxicating life of Paris with those fair ones and dispossessed whom Willy brought so casually to her? Colette bided her time, consciously and subconciously hoarding that raw, crude and obsessive life. How could she have written *Chéri, La Retraite Sentimentale, La Vagabonde, L'Entrave,* and those other nerve-exposing books if she had returned to St-Saveur-en-Puisaye?

Was Willy shocked when, after thirteen years, Colette left him? He does not appear to have been surprised when she packed her books and her treasures and settled down to write on her own. The end of Willy and Colette verges on the farcical. In 1906 Colette, assuming the stage name of René (the obvious derivation of Rénée of *La Vagabonde* and *L'Entrave*), dressed in a London-tailored brown suit, played at the Theatre Royal with Marcel Boulestin and La Marquise de Belbeuf. La Marquise de Belbeuf, whose physical and temperamental characteristics so much resembled those of La Baronne in *Chéri,* was notoriously and outrageously eccentric. Colette's association with La Marquise led to a fantastic first-night scene when the fashionable audience turned on Willy, sitting in a stage box, and abused him for allowing his wife to participate in such an entertainment. So vehement and quixotic was the audience that Willy was forced to appeal for police protection—he, and not Colette, was deemed the villain of this latest scandal. After this their furniture was divided and the question of the division of the *Claudine* royalties debated. Willy, divorced by Colette, continued his exorbitant career until he died in poverty.

After Willy, Colette toured for six years in provincial music-halls, as a dancer and mime until, in 1912, she married Henry de Jouvenal, a newspaper proprietor. Then followed Colette the journalist, dramatic critic, the reporter of boxing matches and murder trials—adding further occupational experience to an already seasoned life.

And what is this love on which Colette squanders such artistry? It is an exposed nerve. A strident insistent theme of sensual desire which has no relation to the simplicity of wedlock and the passivity of family continuity. Woman desiring man, equal in sexual experience and adaptability, both inordinately proud of their prowess. Woman desiring what Colette so aptly calls *la chair fraiche* and which simply cannot be transcribed into other words. Woman knowing woman and man knowing man, and each desiring all that any human body can evoke. It is sex and desire and love and loneliness and tragedy and, above all, it is joy. It is the great admission of sensual pleasure, whether sexual or emotional or hidden like gold below the earth's surface. It is indisputable, not always acknowledged, and courageously presented and shown as one of the greatest glories enjoyed by man, since man possesses imagination and memory and the power to endow both upon his more animal appetites.

To illustrate and describe this love Colette, the artist, brings her sensibility and her experienced appreciation of all that life so closely and intimately links with love. Participator and watcher, Colette knows that love possesses a sensuality beyond the actual physical desire, a sensuality of loss, of departure, of death, of time, of place. Chéri is more than a gigolo because his love for Léa the retired courtesan has developed his perception. Apart from the pure delight of physical satisfaction, contentment and the very chicanery of love, Chéri, in love, knows about the essential loneliness of human relationships, senses the melancholic instability of life, watches the distressing way the seasons have of matching despair and longing, and is one with the streets through which he paces with his grief.

Pigmy Paradise

by COLIN TURNBULL

Illustrated by Diana Mason

IN the centre of the vast African continent there is a small area, hardly two hundred miles across at any point, inhabited by Pigmies. It is on the north-eastern fringe of the Belgian Congo, and here the Ituri forest is at its thickest and most inhospitable. A hundred miles to the west flows the great Congo River, and to the east the Pigmy territory is bordered by the fabulous, snow-capped Mountains of the Moon. Cutting through the middle of the Ituri forest is a long, straight road connecting Stanleyville, on the Congo, with Uganda; but the traveller may well cover its whole length without seeing a real Pigmy.

Many Pigmy seekers never penetrate beyond the small village of Beni, on the extreme edge of the area. This place is a regular Pigmy circus where the little people entice the unwary with their well-rehearsed tricks. But the impact of different cultures and religions has quite changed their way of life. At Beni they have learnt to live without hunting, to earn and spend money, to bow to strange gods and to adopt strange customs. Through intermarriage they lose their distinctive features, and although they are still delightful people they are no longer Pigmies.

When I and my friend passed through Beni we did not spend long there, for we had been told that in the heart of Pigmy country, on the Epulu River, there was a small place run by an American anthropologist, Pat Putnam, and his wife. From all that we had heard of 'Camp Putnam' there was no reason for us to delay at Beni, so, with the great mountains still in sight behind us, we took the road which drops down into the huge Ituri forest.

It was late afternoon when we crossed over the raging, boiling Epulu, and after a short climb up from the far side we came across a curiously incongruous road sign. It pointed down a forest track and said: 'CAMP PUTNAM — DINNERS — ZOO.' This was some three hundred miles from the nearest town. We followed the track, and after passing through a village came into a wide clearing about half a mile from the road. There were a number of small, neat houses to one side, and a little farther away was the main building, overlooking a steep slope which led down to the river's edge.   All were made of mud and roofed with huge Mongongo leaves, three deep, hung like tiles.

Camp Putnam may appear to be the toy of a millionaire, but in fact it is the centre of activities for an earnest, hard-working anthropologist. Pat Putnam first came to the Congo some twenty-five years ago, after graduating from Harvard.   Here he found something which compensated for all the luxuries he might have had in America, and Epulu has been his home now for fifteen years.   He does not try to interfere with either the Africans or the Pigmies, although he has a small hospital for those who want to use it, and is willing to pay good wages if anyone cares to work for him.   Apart from all this, his efforts are directed towards encouraging those around him to lead their own lives, and to pay as little attention as possible to the encroachments of modern civilization.

The Putnams made us welcome and put a fine three-roomed house at our disposal.   Our first encounter with the Pigmies was almost immediately after our arrival, when we witnessed a scene typical of the carefree life these people lead.   An okapi had been trapped, and the meat which had been cut up was waiting for distribution.   Drums, made out of hollow tree trunks, sent out the message, and in no time the clearing was full of excited, shouting, laughing, brown figures— many of them hardly four feet high.   Apart from a small piece of cloth around their waists they wore nothing, except possibly a few beads, and the children were completely naked.   When the meat had been distributed each woman wrapped her share in large leaves,

L

balanced it on her head and ran gaily back into the forest—the men-folk, still laughing and joking, followed more slowly behind.

That night Pat called some of them down and they sat around the open log fire and sang for us. Their singing was quite extraordinary—it showed a subtle appreciation of rhythm and harmony which was infinitely in advance of the African's—but even more striking was the immense vitality these little people showed in their songs. It was a moonlit night and the Epulu River shone clearly through the trees below us. In contrast the fire threw a rosy glow on the already flushed faces. We were enchanted by the scene ; but, as we were soon to learn, it was not quite the genuine thing. Pat confided in us later that 'his' Pigmies were quite accustomed to being called upon to show themselves off to the stray tourist who might penetrate as far as Epulu, but the remarkable thing was that in spite of this their innate simplicity was unspoilt. They regarded it as a joke, and enjoyed being able to show their prowess as actors.

We liked the place and the people so much that we decided to settle down and stay for a month or two. One of the first things we noticed was the tremendous contrast between the Africans and the Pigmies. Apart from size—and some of the Africans are study six-footers—they differ in every possible way. The Africans rejoice in the gifts of civilization. A man will wear a jaunty trilby over a tattered shirt, and keep his almost non-existent trousers up with a bright, plastic belt. His wife will go one better and sport a robe, probably made in Man-chester, decorated with pictures of bicycles, outsize sparking plugs, or with portraits of Mr Churchill and President Truman. The Pigmies, on the contrary, make their own small pieces of cloth from tree bark, dyed in various mixtures of mud and patterned, if at all, with a few spots or stripes. While the African delights in little possessions, the

Pigmy has none. His bark cloth, spear, hunting net and cooking pot are all home-made and easily replaced. He is only tempted by cigarettes and by the brightly coloured beads which sell for a franc a spoonful at the nearest village store. This probably explains why the Africans are to be seen working all day long, whereas the Pigmies just laze about, smoking old cigarette ends stuffed into leaves, idly whittling arrows and spear shafts.

It would have been easy, from the luxury of our mud house, to imagine that we were really getting to know the people around us ; but the pictures we were forming were untrue in one essential point. The Pigmies are not cultivators, and they have no permanent villages of their own. They are hunters and nomads, and their whole life is spent moving from one end of the forest to the other. Those gathered around Camp Putnam were not settled there permanently, and one day they were nowhere to be seen—they had gone off to a hunting camp.

Pat suggested that if we really wanted to get to know the Pigmies, this was our opportunity. These particular Pigmies knew us well by then, and they were willing to have us among them if we were prepared to put up with their way of life. In this way, without any very clear idea of what we were going to, we set out one morning for one of the most extraordinary and delightful experiences I have ever had. Even the long trek through the forest was invigorating, the songs of our guides seeming to infect us with eager anticipation.

After some hours the leaders quickened their steps. In the distance we heard a curious clapping sound, and the unmistakable yodelling of Pigmy singers. Quite suddenly we came into a clearing which seemed to be about two hundred yards across. The trees appeared immeasurably tall, and the sky was completely hidden by a vast leafy roof. On all sides was the seemingly impenetrable forest—a dark, forbidding green—and ahead, the camp.

At first, stupidly looking for the now familiar mud houses, I could see no camp at all. Then I realized that the clearing was surrounded by small huts made out of saplings bent over and covered with leaves— in shape not unlike the Eskimo igloo. To one side a group of Pigmies was busy erecting a veritable palace for the guests ; the sides were left unleafed, but under the wide roof they placed beds, chairs and tables, all made out of twigs and branches. A number of fires burned outside the huts, and in the centre of the camp one large fire sent a great column of smoke up to the tree-tops. It filtered through the leaves, caught up light from the hidden sun beyond, and sent this dancing down to the ground at our feet.   The whole clearing was alive with this magic light.

The Pigmies were in perfect harmony with their surroundings, and were leaping and shouting in a dance of welcome as we entered their home.   They surrounded us and proudly took us to see the house they had built for us.   Then, having made sure that we were comfortable, they returned to their dancing and probably forgot all about us.   They danced for the rest of the afternoon, and would probably have danced on into the night had they not been going out hunting early the next morning.   As it was, they all quietened down after their evening meal, and it was not long before the entire camp was in silence.

We were wakened early and told that we were to be taken net-hunting.   The Pigmies are great hunters.   They live on the meat they get in this way, and exchange the surplus with the Africans for bananas.   Sometimes they will dig deep six-foot pits and cover them over with twigs and leaves, or else they will hunt with bow and arrow. The arrows are often coated with a deadly poison, and to avoid the risk of even scratching themselves the Pigmies keep the tips protected by leaves until the arrows are to be used.   Sometimes three or four Pigmies, the strongest and bravest, will hunt elephant.   For this they are armed only with stout-shafted spears.   On tracking down an elephant they will run up underneath the beast and thrust their spears into its bladder.   If they succeed they know that it will die within two days, so they call to the rest of the camp who come and join in the hunt until they reach the dead animal.

For us, however, it was a net-hunt, and this is the most common method used by the Pigmies.   They make the nets from a special type of vine, and when fully extended each net will stretch to about eighty feet in length, and three feet in height.   On this occasion there were twelve hunters, each armed with a net, a bow and arrow, or a spear. The youngsters went with their fathers, proudly carrying the spear or the net, and the womenfolk followed, chattering gaily, in the rear. After the first mile a " cast " was made, all the nets being tied together and stretched out in a vast semi-circle.   By then the women had stopped gossiping and had taken up their positions as beaters.   When all was ready they closed in towards the nets, yelling, clapping their hands, and making strange noises which apparently indicated to the hunters what sort of animals, if any, were being put up.

The first cast was unsuccessful, but on the second cast two antelope were driven into the nets.   This caused great excitement, and the head Pigmy insisted that I be brought along to witness the execution.   This

was performed with the utmost enjoyment by a young boy, and for a moment I wondered if I could still feel in sympathy with my good friends. But life in the forest leaves no room for sentiment. The killing of animals is not only the profession of the Pigmies but their only means of existence. The larger the catch in any day's hunting the greater their glee, for it means days of idleness ahead.

The Pigmy enjoys his life to the utmost. When he works he enjoys his work and pursues it with all his vigour ; but afterwards he feels himself entitled to a rest, and he will laze about until necessity compels him to work again. The main occupation of all Pigmies, men and women, is hunting ; but after a successful hunt there may be days of inactivity. It was on such days that I felt I was really beginning to know the people. Out hunting the pace was too swift, the excitement too tense, and the thrill too foreign. Since my existence did not depend on the success of the hunt I was on a totally different footing. But the day following the hunt found us all in the same frame of mind. We were tired by the exertions of the previous day, and satisfied at its successful conclusion. The immediate future was assured, and the forest around us wore an air of protective benevolence.

The hunters were sitting about mending their nets or making twine for new ones. Others were busy re-leafing their huts, while some just lay down on the ground near the fires and smoked contentedly. There was a very persistent, hollow tapping sound which I could not trace for a while, until I discovered another clearing near to our own. Here were a number of men sitting down in front of large logs, hammering away with wooden mallets. They were making bark cloth. Nearby was a shallow stream in which the bark had been soaking, and now it was being hammered into strips of remarkably soft 'cloth,' each about three foot by eighteen inches in size. The favourite colour is deep red, but I saw one very fancy piece with bright blue spots.

The chief amusements of the children are tree climbing for the boys and skipping for the girls. In the main part of the camp both were in full swing. The trees seemed alive with agile little brown bodies, and the great game seemed to be for as many as possible to climb to the top of a sapling and so bend it to the ground. They would then all leap off and the sapling would fly upright again, perhaps with one or two stragglers still clinging on.

The skipping and hoop-jumping was charming—the mothers beating the hoops on the ground while the girls, even to the smallest toddler, leapt in and out to a complicated rhythm, singing a little song. I later asked what one of these songs meant, and was told that the children pretend that they are being called to pick bananas. They sing: 'We must go and pick bananas—oh! what the hell, let's skip rope!'

Later on in the afternoon the women all gathered together and while one old man beat at a drum the women danced around in a circle. It seemed to develop into a game of 'follow my leader,' and then I realized that the leading woman was pretending to be a leopard, and all the others were the hunters. The 'leopard' would dance along, prancing from side to side, with some twenty or thirty of her friends behind, imitating her actions. Then suddenly she would turn around and snarl and growl, whereupon all the women would scream and fly behind trees, to emerge a second later shaking with laughter. They were just like delighted children scampering about on a picnic.

But the real joy was in the evening. The camp fires blazed, and after we had all finished our meal we gathered around the large central fire, piled on the logs and sat down. Then the men started telling stories of the great hunting expeditions that they and their fathers had made, of deeds of great valour, and of the many dangers they had come through. This worked itself up into a dance—a superb firelight dance—in which all the great feats of yesterday were re-enacted. I sat spellbound as the flames flickered and threw shadows of gigantic Pigmies across the forest floor. Their handsome, eager faces were flushed with delight, and their eyes were seeing scenes that I would never see. They danced and sang, sometimes singly and sometimes all together. Around that one fire the whole story of their forest life unfolded.

The frenzy of their excitement was magnificent. These little people, and the immense forest their very own. They threw out their chests and thrust imaginary spears at imaginary elephants, singing and stamping all the time. As soon as one sat down another would leap up, until impatience overtook them and they all hurled their boasts of defiance at the darkness together, dancing in a wild circle about the fire; twisting, turning and jumping, clapping their hands, throwing back their heads and singing with all their might.

It must have been early morning when the fires died down and the revellers dropped, one by one, through sheer exhaustion. It was a long time before I could get to sleep. For a brief, bewitching moment I had seen with Pigmy eyes: I wanted to hold on to that moment for as long as possible. The sound of that delightful, irresponsible song still rings in my ears: 'What the hell, let's skip rope!'; and when I close my mind to the clamour of civilization I can still see those mighty little men dancing arrogantly in all the splendour of uncivilization.

Sun and Fun

SONG OF A NIGHT-CLUB PROPRIETRESS

I walked into the night club in the morning,
  There was kümmel on the handle of the door,
The ashtrays were unemptied,
The cleaning unattempted,
  And a squashed tomato sandwich on the floor.

I pulled aside the thick magenta curtains
  —So Regency, so Regency, my dear—
And a host of little spiders
Ran a race across the ciders
  To a box of baby 'pollies by the beer.

Oh sun upon the summer-going by-pass
  Where ev'rything is speeding to the sea,
And wonder beyond wonder
That here where lorries thunder
  The sun should ever percolate to me.

When Boris used to call in his Sedanca,
  When Teddy took me down to his estate,
When my nose excited passion,
When my clothes were in the fashion,
  When my beaux were never cross if I was late,

There was sun enough for lazing upon beaches,
  There was fun enough for far into the night.
But I'm dying, dear, and done for,
What on earth was all the fun for?
  Draw the curtains, shut the sunlight out of sight.

JOHN BETJEMAN

Drawings by Ronald Searle

The 'Twenties

by JAMES LAVER

Tᴉᴍᴇ is a stream. We cannot cut it up into lengths as if it were a roll of cloth, and yet we cannot resist the temptation to insert our futile scissors and to imagine we have something we can hold up and say: 'This is the nineteenth century!' or 'Here are the 'Twenties.' Perhaps we may be forgiven, if only because we cannot help it. The mind has need of these devices, and if we remember that our divisions are quite arbitrary perhaps no great harm is done.

Certain epochs do seem to emerge as entities; we fancy we can discern a pattern, make some sort of pretence of perceiving a beginning and an end; and perhaps for those who were young in the 'Twenties the illusion is easier. Dean Inge once remarked that every man is a man of the decade when he himself was between twenty and thirty. If that be so the Dean remains still a 'Man of the 'Eighties' and the present writer is a 'Man of the 'Twenties,' and all his efforts to keep up with the times will never make him anything else.

Of course the 'Twenties are now under a cloud. It takes about thirty years (just a generation) for any period to cross the 'gap in appreciation,' to emerge from the darkness which follows every art-form like its own shadow. We cannot possibly admire the décor and costume of the 'Twenties : they are too near to us in time. Its interior furnishings seem to us ugly and its dresses absurd. Show any woman a fashionable dress of 1925, with its straight lines, its low waist and its beige tint, and she will cry out in horror. Such dresses could surely never have been made by fashionable dressmakers, never considered *chic*. They were! And they will be again, but for the moment we find it hard to believe it.

Looking through the newspaper files and illustrated magazines of the period, we find a world which is at once oddly like our own and strangely different. Some things which we take for granted, like radio and trans-Atlantic flights, were only in their beginnings. Sir Ross Smith was hitting the headlines by flying to Australia ; Sir John Alcock, fresh from his Atlantic triumph, had just been killed in an accident near Rouen. Someone had flown at 150 miles an hour.

It was the day of the crystal set and '2LO.' People were still so much excited by the discovery that they could hear across the aether that they didn't very much care what. Radio critics had not yet been thought of. The cinema was still gesticulating in dumb show, although there were already experiments in the 'talking picture,' not to come to fruition for another decade.

It is perhaps reasurring to note that the world seemed to be in almost as bad shape as it is today. Peace had just been signed but *'les guerres de la paix'* continued to rage. There was a Greek war in Asia Minor. D'Annunzio was still in occupation of Fiume and was defying the 'Powers' to get him out. The Bolsheviks were advancing into Siberia ; the French occupied Frankfurt. There was shooting in Amritsar, street-fighting in Berlin, and, of course, 'trouble' in Ireland where the Sinn Feiners had just made the unfortunate discovery that there is no answer to terrorism. In England there was a coal-strike, and rioting among the unemployed in London.

But it was not these things that took up most of the space in the papers. There were fashionable weddings (two kings attended the nuptials of Sir Oswald Mosley), the departure of the Prince of Wales for Australia, the smash hit of *Irene,* Sybil Thorndike as Medea. Mary Pickford was boomed as the World's Sweetheart. There were winter sports and Dalcroze Eurythmics, *The Young Visiters* and Epstein's 'Christ.' The Empress Eugénie, that strange *survivante,* died at last,

Joan of Arc was made a saint, and Suzanne Lenglen became lady lawn tennis champion of the world.

Social life took up again, or tried to take up again, at the point where it had left off when Germany tore up the 'Scrap of Paper' and the field-grey battalions came flooding into France. There were supper-parties again at the Savoy and thé-dansants at all the best hotels in London. Some of them even put on cabarets where the 'girls' were supposed to be daringly unclothed, although when one looks at their photographs now there doesn't seem to be anything very daring about it. The young generations, those who were just back from the War and those that had grown up while it was raging, seemed to be determined to enjoy themselves and to make up for lost time. Nothing 'stuffy' was henceforward to be tolerated, and the adjective 'Victorian' —largely owing to the success of Lytton Strachey's book—became one of unqualified abuse.

This was perhaps the only point at which the 'gay' world touched hands with the Intellectuals. These too were determined that nothing Victorian should be given a moment's hearing. The War, which had carried away so many of the young, had been entirely the fault of the old men, the pompous and platitudinous politicians who (such was the theory) had sat comfortably at home while the casualty lists lengthened and the heap of 'riddled corpses round Bapaume' grew higher and higher. There was a new malaise in the world of the intelligentsia. The mood in which Rupert Brooke had set out contrasted strongly with the mood in which Siegfried Sassoon had come home. The world of idealism had been destroyed and instead there was a Waste Land, a kind of lunar landscape like that shown in the canvases which Paul Nash had brought back from the Front.

Instead of the World Fit for Heroes to Live in promised by Lloyd George, there was an acute housing shortage and long lines of unemployed men queuing up for the dole. Instead of a return to normal conditions (whatever such a phrase means or has ever meant) there was unrest and discontent everywhere. Among intellectuals the belief in progress had received a rude jar, and their growing scepticism was expressed in incisive phrases by that remarkable cleric, the Dean of St. Paul's. Richard Aldington voiced the bitter disappointment of all those who had hoped that the sacrifices of so much young life would not have been in vain.

But the dominant mood of the 'Twenties was quite different. Most of the young men back from the War were not intellectuals and would indeed have been highly insulted if anyone had suggested that they were. To them Aldington and Sassoon and the Gloomy Dean (as they characteristically called him) were simply people who did not know how to enjoy themselves. The people who could afford it (and there were more of them than there are today, for confiscatory taxation was only just beginning) flung themselves into a life of gaiety, hectic perhaps, but enjoyable enough while it lasted. The War had been terrible, but it was over and, since it had been a 'war to end wars,' it could obviously never happen again. The League of Nations was ridiculed, but people believed in it all the same. The world had plenty of troubles, no doubt. Let the politicians look to them. Meanwhile, 'let's have fun.'

One would have to go back to the days of the French *Directoire* to find another period of the same mood and tempo. After the fall of Robespierre Paris went mad with gaiety. The cry was pleasure at all costs and the dancing mania was universal. A similar dancing mania characterized the 'Twenties. People danced all night and almost all day, and the improvement in gramophones made it possible to turn on the music at any hour. Jazz was known before the War, but it now became the only rhythm. And the dances were of course negro dances.

It is an extraordinary thing that no sophisticated (one is tempted to say, no civilized) person can invent a dance. All he can do is to take some peasant dance (the dance, that is, of people who have not yet lost all *gaîeté de cœur*) and make it just sufficiently decent for the ballroom floor. Gradually through the nineteenth century the upper classes had absorbed the peasant dances of Europe, had taken over the waltzes and mazurkas that had once provided the merrymaking in the villages of Poland and Hungary. In the early twentieth century there were no more left. There was only the negro to go to. So, in the 'Twenties, the Charleston and the Black Bottom spread like a prairie fire, and the gestures of the dancers in the smart restaurants of London and Paris were so many echoes of the jungle.

We have said the *restaurants* of London and Paris, for dancing, as in the period of the *Directoire,* had become a public affair. Dances still took place in private houses, sometimes almost confessedly as a final occasion, as in the splendid eighteenth-century ball given in Devonshire House just before it was demolished. But in general people danced in restaurants, and restaurants, unlike private houses, are open to anyone who has money to pay. The disintegration of 'Society' which had been proceeding ever since Edwardian days, was noticeably speeded up. The *chic* replaced the *comme il faut* ; the 'gorgeous fringes' spread over the entire warp and woof. For the first time we hear the gigolo spoken of, perhaps with a shrug, but without any simulated horror. The *divorcée* and the woman with no visible means of support are alike accepted. The catchword is 'amusing,' and if that hurdle can be taken—anything goes.

It was not of course that the 'Twenties were more 'immoral' than the epochs that had gone before. It was only that things had got a little bit more mixed up. The Edwardian man of the world kept his life in watertight compartments and was even pedantically careful that his wife and his mistress should never meet. In the 'Twenties all the barriers were down. There were no more *grandes cocottes*; a general promiscuity had deprived them of their status and even of their livelihood.

> *In the days of more strict propriety*
> *Women like me were covered with glory;*
> *But now, since these damned Society women*
> *Invaded my territory. . . .*
>
> *A busted, disgusted cocotte am I,*
> *On the page of this age just a blot am I,*
> *For since the girls called chic*
> *Have invented new technique,*
> *I'm afraid, at my trade, not so hot am I. . . .*

As Cole Porter was to sing at the end of our period. And the dominant type was now very different from the fine woman of the Edwardian epoch, so different that she almost seemed to belong to another breed.

Once more one has to go back to the years following the French Revolution to find her like. In both periods women cut off their hair, straightened the lines of the figure as far as Nature would allow—and sometimes even further, threw away their corsets, and wore their waists in the wrong place : very high in 1800, very low in 1925. They also took the colour out of their clothes. Dresses were white after the French Revolution ; the 'Twenties was the era of beige.

Rather cynically, it has been called the ghost of khaki; but whatever it was it spread over everything. Dresses were beige, carpets and curtains were beige; even the complexions were beige. It seems to be a psychological law that emancipated women cannot wear bright colours. Nor, it seems, can they have their waists in the right place.

The waist round the hips was indeed characteristic of the 'Twenties and the effect was emphasized by the extremely short skirts which came in in 1925. Before that the dresses had been tubular, but long. Now they rose to the knees. For the first time in history, at least since primitive times, women showed their legs in public, legs clothed, also for the first time, in flesh-coloured stockings which enhanced the effect of nakedness. When they danced, or sat down and crossed their legs, their bare thighs were sometimes visible, and old gentlemen who in Edward's reign had found a mere ankle stimulating enough now began to die in large numbers as a result of this new excitement. Certainly if a woman of 1925 had walked out into the streets in 1905 she would have been run in by the police.

On the other hand there was an extreme reticence about the bosom. It was not supposed to exist, and young women who found it difficult to conform to the prevailing flat-chested mode even purchased 'flatteners' to destroy the natural curves with which they had been endowed. This was, in its way, an even more violent mutilation than tight-lacing and almost equally deleterious.

Morally, it was probably more so, for tight-lacing does imply a certain *tenue* and restraint. Tight-laced epochs are—tight-laced. No-corset epochs tend to be loose in both senses of the word. And the 'Twenties were certainly 'loose.' The chaperone was discarded as a Victorian joke, and, at least in the sets that made the pace, virginity was almost a term of abuse. Even young girls took to drinking spirits, sometimes in considerable quantities, and some of them did not stop at spirits in order to get the kick without which life hardly seemed worth living. A contemporary versifier has endeavoured to paint a picture of the Woman of the 'Twenties which we must accept as not far from the truth :

> *Mother's advice, and Father's fears*
> *Alike are voted—just a bore*
> *There's negro music in our ears,*
> *The world is one huge dancing floor,*
> *We mean to tread the Primrose Path,*
> *In spite of Mr Joynson Hicks.*
> *We're People of the Aftermath,*
> *We're girls of 1926.*
>
> *In greedy haste, on pleasure bent,*
> *We have no time to think, or feel.*
> *What need is there for sentiment,*
> *Now we've invented Sex-Appeal?*

We've silken legs and scarlet lips,
We're young and hungry, wild and free.
Our waists are round about the hips,
Our skirts are well above the knee.

We've boyish busts and Eton crops,
We quiver to the saxophone.
Come, dance before the music stops,
And who can bear to be alone?
Come drink your gin, or sniff your 'snow,'
Since Youth is brief, and Love has wings,
And Time will tarnish, e'er we know
The brightness of the Bright Young Things.

Perhaps future historians will wonder who those Bright Young Things might be who made so much noise in the world during their brief and hectic career. In their day they were the delight of Fleet Street, where their antics provided an almost daily ration of copy, and the despair of all right-thinking people, of all those, that is, who still had the capacity for being shocked at anything. They gave wild parties, with titles in which ingenuity and sheer silliness battled for the prize. 'Come as your dearest enemy,' 'come as your opposite,' 'come as your secret self' : such were the themes of these junketings of self-expression and self-advertisement. But the height, or the depth, was reached by the famous Baby Party, at which grown men and women appeared in various stages of infancy, and pushed one another in perambulators round a well-known London square.

A surprising amount of indignation was caused by this escapade. It was described as an outrage on the public and as an insult to the innocence of childhood—as indeed it was. For innocence was hardly the outstanding quality of the Bright Young Things. On the contrary, they paraded their vices, they

> *'drank, and drugged, and stole each other's men —*
> *It was the fashion, then.'*

They became involved in car crashes between one road house and another, they were picked up drunk in the gutters of Jermyn Street. A few of them—the toughest—have survived into our own day. They have settled down, and one or two have even set up as guardians of modern morality, denouncing the sins and follies of a new generation. Most of them are dead.

Fashions of the 'Twenties

Mary Pickford (*above*) was still the World's Sweetheart, despite the discovery by Clara Bow (*right*) of a hitherto unmentionable quality termed It

On the left, Nigel Bruce gazes enrapt at the exquisite Eton Crop worn by Gladys Cooper at the Playhouse in 1928. *Below*, a Bright Young Person demonstrates the freedom of the new Smoking Slacks for Women, 1922

What we think of as the 'Twenties was in fact a very brief period—less than a decade. Already in 1926 the General Strike had given a rude shock to public complacency, and before the 'Thirties dawned the shadows had begun to close in. What really put an end to the picnic was the American Slump.

America and England—such was the theory—were perfectly sound financially. Continental countries might have troubles with their currency, but this was a positive advantage, since it enabled Anglo-Saxons to have holidays abroad almost for nothing. People told one another stories of living in Austrian hotels for a shilling a day. The fluctuation of the French franc enabled one to enjoy, at a cheap rate, all the pleasures of a holiday on the Riviera, no longer in winter, as the benighted Edwardians had imagined, but all the year round. For the new woman of the 'Twenties no longer protected her complexion with a sunshade. Rather she lay, as naked as possible, stretched out at Eden Roc, acquiring the tint of a burnt biscuit. The Lido at Venice, from having been a mere strip of sand frequented by middle-class Italians, suddenly became a fashionable resort. Some of the Bright Young Things transferred their activities thither, and succeeded in shocking Mussolini.

It was a halcyon period if only because people saw no reason why it should not go on for ever. It was brought to an end by the lengthening bread-lines in America and the growing menace of German arms. Suddenly people woke up to the fact that peace was not something they could take for granted, that prosperity was not automatic but had to be won by wisdom and hard work, that the race was still to the swift and the battle to the strong, that national survival depended upon national *virtue*, in the widest sense of the word. Perhaps the despised Victorians had not been so far wrong after all? It was a disquieting thought, for it meant that the party was over, and that someone had to wash-up. We have been washing-up ever since, and some of us who were young in the 'Twenties cannot escape from an occasional pang of nostalgia for a period of gaiety, however hectic, and of hope, however delusive. In the individual life there is often a short gap when one has escaped from tutelage and not yet assumed the burdens of responsibility, when the world seems full of pleasures not yet savoured and it is permissible to be a little wild. The 'Twenties was the undergraduate age of the modern world ; or are we old fogies simply talking of ourselves?

M

The Blithe Spirit of the 'Twenties

by J. W. LAMBERT

'THE 'Twenties,' I heard myself saying, in fine, ringing tones, 'the brittle, bright and beastly 'Twenties! What a decade—brilliant I dare say, but how self-conscious, how sterile! The jazz age, the cocktail age! The age of the gossip-writers! A society of feverish automata, with Noel Coward as its laureate and scourge. . . .'

My host, a man of fifty, leaned forward ; before he spoke I knew, only too well, what he was going to say.

'And what precisely, my boy, do you know about the 'Twenties?'

All the same there was, I assured myself as I walked home, something in what I had said. Not everyone in Charles II's England was a Rochester or a Lady Castlemaine, but the word 'Restoration' surely deserves its overtones of sprightly vice ; not everyone in the days of George III's madness was a Lord George Hell, yet the word 'Regency' cannot fail to suggest a certain exuberant debauchery ; the 'Nineties were doubtless not as naughty as all that, despite dreary Beardsley, doleful Dowson and the cut-price beauties of the Empire Promenade. And the 'Twenties—didn't they deserve their reputation for cheap iconoclasm and rather impetuous pleasure-seeking?

And do not the works of Noel Coward exactly epitomize the desperately blithe spirit of those days? He has done his best to illuminate the point for younger generations, for in many respects he seems hardly to have changed at all. His work has changed, of course : at the end of the 'Twenties it suffered a great purge, and since then it has progressively softened, or, perhaps one should say, mellowed. In 1926, for example, he gave us in *Easy Virtue* a study of an English family, approximately 'county,' suffering severe moral defeat at the hands of a young woman with a foreign accent and no great pretensions to respectability ; in 1951 he used the same situation in *Relative Values,* but awarded the victory to the family—true-blue 'county' by this time. Yet, the shift of emphasis apart, these two plays might have been written within a few weeks of each other.

236

In his own public personality, too, he seems to embody, in an age-less way, the glamour of another time ; he keeps his fallen day about him.   The slim figure, neat, controlled, calm, seems to shiver every now and then with nervous tension.   The head is a carefully composed work of art.   Let us examine it closely : what the upper lip promises of precise, objective comment, the lower qualifies with a warmer full-ness, equally apt to affection, petulance or sheer vulgarity ; then, when he smiles, the corners of his mouth go not up, but ruefully down ; the nose, not precisely long, has a certain terrier-like quality ; the large, fleshy ears, and the hair so flattened against the skull that it might almost have been painted on, lend the face beneath them the hypnotic aloofness of a ventriloquist's doll ; the eyes are large and bright and bland, and receive more than they give.   Yet the most exquisitely dated thing about him, his most highly individual attribute, is his voice.   It is a young, tired voice ; light, sharp and dry, it rings constant subtle changes on a few highly-charged inflections.   There is no sensuous warmth about it, not much suggestion of ease or relaxation.   It is the very voice of an age which abandoned belief and reticence, but remained superstitious and tongue-tied—the voice of the 'Twenties :

> *We are the hollow men*
> *We are the stuffed men*
> *Leaning together*
> *Headpieces filled with straw.   Alas !*
> *Our dried voices, when*
> *We whisper together*
> *Are quiet and meaningless*
> *As wind in dry grass*
> *Or rats' feet over broken glass*
> *In our dry cellar*

—thus T. S. Eliot, with an air of chilly resignation, washes his hands of them in perpetual dew.

Theirs was a world of febrile triviality, and nowhere more so than in the world of the arts, which was rapidly declining into a world of culture.   The old guard soldiered on, most of them rather lost, but the newcomers listened to the zombie-voices from across the Channel, the aggressive nihilists from a shattered Europe ; or scurried into pattern-making as a relief from thought and observation ; or peered into the depths of human personality and naturally found it extremely un-congenial ; or they cultivated an ingrowing sensibility ; or they pro-claimed that we must smash the machines.   Very few of them plunged into the new, rich, flashy whirl which was to give the period its hall-mark, and most of those who did either killed themselves, or soon hurried into the shelter of other-worldly aspirations.

The theatre, it is true, though especially vulnerable, survived the ordeal pretty well, largely because it was, as usual, behind the times. There were many active dramatists of a quality rare today, but the better of them—Galsworthy and St John Ervine, even Maugham and Lonsdale—spoke, in very varied accents, with pre-war voices. As for the best of them, the decade which gave us *Saint Joan* and *Juno and the Paycock* is not to be despised ; but these are not plays of any particular period. When I talk to senile friends in their forties I find that it is the lighter, brighter nothings of their youth which draw a reminiscent tear—*The Beggar's Opera* or *Riverside Nights*, perhaps, Nigel Playfair's happy concoctions at the Lyric Theatre, Hammersmith ; and they are quite lost to the passage of time at the thought of Charlot's revues, and better still Cochran's series at the London Pavilion, of the *Black Birds,* the *Chauve-Souris,* or the *Co-Optimists*—two exotics and a barnyard rooster. Or they fondly recall Edna Best in *The Constant Nymph ;* or Cedric Hardwicke's rural saws in *Yellow Sands ;* or *The Green Hat,* a quite fantastic period piece about a nymphomaniac, a triumph for Tallulah Bankhead, that green-eyed, husky American legend ; her peculiar gift it was to attract the adoration not only of the men but of the women in the audience.

As usual, those who were busy giving the new age its individuality were sharply at odds with those who felt sure that the country was going to the bad. Running with the former, and hunting with the latter, we discern the agile figure of Mr Coward. He became a national figure at the age of twenty-five, when *The Vortex* was produced at the Everyman Theatre, Hampstead, in November, 1924. He was even before then by no means unknown. He had been on the stage since he was ten ; Miss Italia Conti had noticed him, Charles Hawtrey had noticed him, Nigel Playfair had noticed him. He had been a writer almost as long, and had turned out several plays and magazine stories, many songs—and a volume of burlesque memoirs by imaginary courtesans, of which the title, *A Withered Nosegay,* seems an adequate record. Nor had he neglected his social obligations, for he was already on excellent terms with a number of titled persons, and had visited several tolerably stately homes. Two of his plays, *I'll Leave It to You* and *The Young Idea,* had already been produced and well-spoken of. By his share—roughly that of Pooh-Bah in the state offices of Titipu—in Charlot's revue, *London Calling,* he had

First stages in the cavalcade of success. *On the right:* the beginnings of a notable partnership—Noel Coward and Gertrude Lawrence burlesque the Astaires in 'London Calling,' 1923. *Above:* the precocious playwright of twenty-five receives breakfast-time congratulations on the success of 'The Vortex.' *Below:* with 'No, No, Nanette' on the music stand, Noel Coward dictates a revue lyric to his secretary, 1925. (*Photos from Raymond Mander and Joe Mitchenson Collection*)

Tallulah Bankhead and Edna Best (*left*) shocked the town as they tippled through 'Fallen Angels,' 1925, but the amorous gymnastics of Ivor Novello and Frances Doble (*below*), in 'Sirocco,' were booed by the first-night audience two years later. Between-whiles the author took over to New York the 1925 Rolls Royce which he bought out of the royalties on 'The Vortex.' (*Raymond Mander and Joe Mitchenson Collection*)

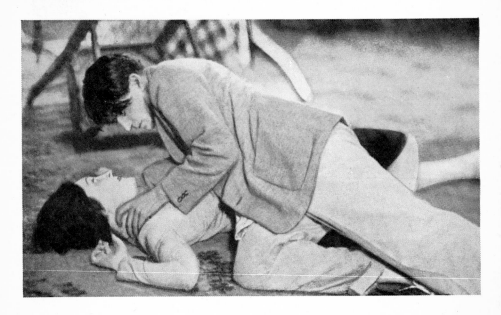

positively demanded attention ; and got it, in the shape of the following remarkable comment from James Agate :

For years the critics have complained that the people who produce revues persistently ignore the wits while paying attention to the wigs. . . . Latterly there have been signs of a change, and in his present venture Mr André Charlot has gone to the length of impressing, in the person of Mr Noel Coward, the youngest and who shall say that does not mean the brainiest, of our intellectuals . . . there is no wit like that of a highbrow who is really witty.

Intellectual? Highbrow? Are we speaking of the same man? Well, he has been accused of worse than that in his time. Perhaps this curious estimate was prompted by the most immediately striking of the burlesques Mr Coward contributed to the revue—the celebrated *Swiss Family Whittlebot* :

Miss Hernia Whittlebot should be effectively and charmingly dressed in undraped dyed sacking, a cross between blue and green, with a necklet of uncut amber beads in unconventional shapes. She must wear a gold band rather high up on her forehead, from which hang (*sic*) a little clump of Bacchanalian fruit below each ear. Her face is white and weary, with a long chin and nose, and bags under the eyes. . . .

After explaining the family's views on the Inevitable Truth in Rhythmic Colour Poetry, 'I will now recite,' says Miss Whittlebot, 'my tone poem "Passion," to which special music has been set by my brother Gob on the Cophutican' :

> *Passion's dregs are the salt of life*
> *Spirits trodden beneath the heel of*
> *Ingratitude.*
> *Drains and sewers support the quest*
> *Of eternal indulgence.*
> *Thank God for the Coldstream Guards.*

Crude, perhaps, but pointed ; and nobody was in any doubt about the originals—least of all the originals themselves, who were terribly cross, and remained so for several years.

Thus, by fits and starts, young Mr Coward had been working his way forward ; and, when the curtain fell to tremendous cheers after that first performance of *The Vortex,* he reached at a bound the utmost pinnacle of fame—he was asked his opinion of the modern girl, and had his wardrobe imitated by admiring youths.

As one peers back at it from the 1950s *The Vortex* seems excessively melodramatic ; it is difficult not to put it in the same pigeon-hole as *East Lynne* or Douglas Jerrold's *Fifteen Years in a Drunkard's Life.* A recent revival drove the point home ; still, we were able to laugh at most of the jokes and all the clothes. But evidently it struck loud and clear the dominant, if not typical, note of the time. Here was the unseemly and unrewarding chase after pleasure ; the spectacle of an ageing woman flaunting her folly with a young lover ; the frittering of talent in a haze of alcohol, cigarette-smoke and drugs ; the automatic dancing, the discordant smartness of interior decoration 'on the verge of being original' ; the reproaches of the abandoned young hurled at the head of an elder generation equally abandoned in a different sense—all presented with great theatrical skill in a new tone of voice: light-weight dialogue fired in short bursts, as opposed to the rumbling cannonades of the old brigade or the calculated mortar-fire of the epigrammatists.

Enthroned as the young master of London's revels, Mr Coward poured out plays and revues ; his name was in almost every issue of every paper ; socially, his first nights surpassed all others in brilliance. While *The Vortex* was still running came *On With the Dance,* the first of the Coward–Cochran revues, *Fallen Angels* and *Hay Fever* ; and then *Easy Virtue, The Queen Was in the Parlour, The Marquise, Home Chat, Sirocco, This Year of Grace.* He wrote also a piece called *Semi-Monde,* set in the Ritz bar in Paris, which he knew could never be produced in an English-speaking country ; and *This Was a Man,* which was promptly banned in Britain, though performed with indifferent success in Berlin, Paris and New York.

Behind this list of titles lies another drama—the stormy emotional relationship between the great British public and Mr Coward himself. If when he parodied the Sitwells he was mistaken for an intellectual, all the more when he depicted vice was he assumed to be himself a creature of enormous depravity—which was at any rate excellent publicity. Moreover, the sophisticated world might lick its weals after Mr Coward's minatory strokes, but it also licked its lips and asked for more. This was too much: the thunder rumbled, the lightning flickered, and soon Mr Coward was caught in a deluge of advice, admonition and abuse.

In 1922 James Agate was hailing him as a welcome intellectual recruit to the lighter stage. In 1925, apropos *Fallen Angels,* he thought that 'the extravaganza—for that is what this play really is—shows not a nasty mind, but a juvenile pre-occupation with nasty things common to young people at the age of puberty.' Of *Hay Fever* he had a different suggestion to make : 'Will not Mr Coward forget all about that which he vaguely deems to be "Society" and go down to Southend and spend a week among dead winkles and living people?' And then, of *Easy Virtue,* the old complaint—' "There are moments, are there not, when one doesn't think of girls?" Mr Beerbohm made Mr George Moore say in his pastiche. But there are no moments, apparently, in which Mr Coward, the dramatist, refrains from thinking in terms of sex.'

There were at least three very good reasons why. To take the lowest first, Mr Coward himself explains the point very clearly in *This Was a Man :*

> *Zoe :* I really came to ask you to dine tonight and go to a play.
> *Edward :* I'd love to. What do you want to see?
> *Zoe :* A nice clean play, please, Edward.
> *Edward :* Splendid. We shan't have any trouble getting seats.

Then of course something spiced with wickedness was expected of him ; and lastly, the subject was very much in the air. In the works of a man acclaimed as the mirror of his age, or even of half his age, sex was bound to feature rather prominently. The war had left behind it feelings of guilt and futility ; it had also brought freedom, some said, from the shackles of an outworn scale of values, freedom to explore and experiment with life. Oddly enough this turned out to mean hardly more than freedom to experiment with love. With Havelock Ellis, Freud, and Frazer its Holy Writ, Dr Marie Stopes and Bertrand Russell its prophets, and the untrammelled pastures of the Trobriand Islands its promised land, free love gained converts by the thousand, a conscientious band ; the divorce rate soared, anxiety neuroses bloomed more freely than Flanders poppies, and content was no more than a whisper of the wind in the willows.

An oddly-phrased, and apparently contradictory, variant of the view that Mr Coward's plays had too much sex in them came from a critic in *The Morning Post,* who enquired 'What manly actors could be happy as Mr Coward's men, who are denuded of almost all manly characteristics?' But as box-office receipts rose, words like 'nauseating,' 'obscene' and 'vile' rose also in a thickening cloud. Next, inevitably,

James Douglas trumpeted his commination. The 'Twenties, to balance their free love, were alive with pornography-hounds, and Douglas was one of the most assiduous of them. In the columns of a very popular newspaper he brayed forth his discoveries in terms from which his victims might well have shrunk. Having described Aldous Huxley as 'a hog of genius' and 'a blowfly,' he soon found it necessary to warn readers that 'Mr Noel Coward excites and titillates by shovelling up the ordure of an unprincipled smart set.' If true, this would cast a most curious light upon the taste of the time.

Gradually, then suddenly, the public turned against him. In 1927 *Home Chat,* a very trivial and rather flat piece about adultery, appeared and was roundly booed. Then came the famous first night of *Sirocco,* at which trouble was brewing from the start. There seems to be little in this slightly tawdry tale of boredom, stupidity and weakness to excite or titillate, and its characters are not even smart, but it was very roughly handled. When Mr Coward came on the stage to share the final uproar he personally was booed for seven minutes. The unfortunate leading lady, Frances Doble, stepped forward to announce tearfully that this was the happiest night of her life ; Mr Coward and Ivor Novello, his leading man, burst out laughing, and pandemonium set in again. When the author tried to speak a gentleman in the stalls rose and shouted, 'Shut up, you swine!' and another cried, 'Un-English! Un-English!' And when Mr Coward left the theatre he did so through a hostile crowd, several members of which spat upon him as he passed.

Well-meaning defenders meanwhile hurried to the rescue. Miss G. B. Stern, for one, pointed out that 'the subtle joke about him is that he is an extremely severe preacher, and every play he writes is a moral sermon' ; and again 'he is fundamentally a Savonarola . . . he is Brother Praise-the-Lord, fallen accidentally into our own times from the Cromwellian period.' Miss Stern, too, may have toyed with overstatement, but she was nearer the mark than Douglas. It is true that today *The Vortex* seems a laboriously moral tale ; that even in *Fallen Angels* the tipsy women awaiting their lovers soliloquize about their motives in homely terms ; that in nearly all the plays smugness and hypocrisy are belaboured. It is true that a song like *Poor Little Rich Girl,* one of the most successful of its time, by no means presents its heroine as deliriously happy :

> *You're only a baby*
> *You're lonely, and maybe*

Someday soon you'll know
The years you are tasting
Are years you are wasting.
* Life is a bitter foe ;*
With fate it's no use competing
Youth is so terribly fleeting ;
By dancing much faster
You're chancing disaster,
* Time alone will show.*

Not happy, no . . . but still, romantic.   They are mostly romantic, or exciting, or clever and amusing, his characters, however vicious. There's the rub.

Several Mr Cowards had a hand in shaping them—Mr Coward the man of the world, Mr Coward the man of the theatre, and, never quite elbowed out of the picture, Mr Coward of, let us say, Clapham Common and the quiet life.   Perhaps, when he had fought his way up from his middle-class suburban background into Society, he was disappointed not to find there the comfortable virtues of family life, transmuted by wealth and leisure into what the advertisements called Gracious Living.   Alas!   If Society had ever offered that commodity, it certainly did not by the time he got there.   It no longer consisted of an aristocracy leavened by rising members of the middle classes, but of the much-enriched middle classes themselves, decorated with such members of the aristocracy as cared to join in ; and, thus reconstituted, rushed yelling like children out of school into the playground of metropolitan delights.   If Mr Coward, among the roysterers, was Brother Praise-the-Lord, he seems to have come, as a dramatist, perilously close to the position of the parson in Maugham's *Rain,* who denounced with the greatest fervour those aspects of life which he found it most difficult to resist.   Perhaps the public sensed this ambivalence, and resented it.

But quickly the quarrel was patched up, and soon it was forgotten. First he dazzled with *This Year of Grace* ; he soothed with *Bitter Sweet* ; and then he risked a return to the old manner with *Private Lives*—but by this time he had come to terms with life ; the play has no taint of puritanical nagging, and is therefore not in the least unsavoury.   It is also one of his very best plays, and it triumphed.

By now the 'Twenties were ebbing away.   The day of bitter little personal moralities was done ; the day of bumble-headed public moralities was at hand.   Mr Coward, a changed man, could look forward to the sophisticated joys of *Design for Living, Blithe Spirit,* and *Present Laughter.* But more than a change of tone was in the air ; the nation was rocking on its foundations, and Mr Coward of Clapham Common insisted on a hearing. Falling-in the man of the world and the man of the theatre smartly behind him, he wrote, in the only vein through which he has ever succeeded in driving a flow of genuine emotion, *Cavalcade.* This time the family—a family with small children—went to Bognor, not Deauville ; eyes brimmed with tears as the little Queen's coffin went by ; men worked and women wept. The 'Twenties, the hectic, desperate, pioneering 'Twenties, were not mentioned at all save in that sad little epilogue :

> *Blues, Twentieth Century Blues, are getting me down*
> *Who's escaped those weary Twentieth Century Blues ?*
> *Why, if there's a God up in the sky, shouldn't he grin ?*
> *High above this dreary Twentieth Century din.*

That was the last banshee wail of the 'Twenties, and it should have been the end of *Cavalcade.* But Mr Coward the man of the theatre naturally could not bring himself to ring down the curtain upon that note ; aided and abetted by Mr Coward of Clapham Common, he pushed aside Mr Coward the man of the world, and contrived the remarkable scene in which, from a silent, darkened stage 'away at the back a Union Jack glows through the blackness. The lights slowly come up and the whole stage is composed of massive tiers, upon which stand the entire company. The Union Jack flies over their heads as they sing "God Save the King." ' And who shall say which Mr Coward tremulously said, to end his first-night speech : 'I hope that this play has made you feel that in spite of the troublous times we are living in, it is still pretty exciting to be English'?

Since then we have come to know that we can rely on whichever Mr Coward it is to come forward in moments of crisis, to celebrate our national qualities with a *Cavalcade, This Happy Breed,* or *In Which We Serve.* Now we need Mr Coward the man of the world, whom Sir Desmond MacCarthy aptly compared to 'one of those water-spiders that skate on the surface of a stream but never get into the water—if they did, they would be done for.' Long may he skate on, to remind us of what was best in those brittle, bright, and beastly 'Twenties—vivacity, quick-wittedness, youthfulness of spirit—even a little garishness wouldn't come amiss. We're a solemn lot, nowadays.

The Golden Age of Sport

by HOWARD MARSHALL

I SUPPOSE we all see the days of our youth, our own playing days, as the golden age of sport. I feel like that about the Nineteen-twenties, though I know well enough that this will involve me in much argument. The giants walked then, or so it seems to me, though I realize how dangerous it is to use a magnifying glass on our legendary heroes.

Still, the names mean something, unless our memories are very short. Look at that scowling, unshaven pugilist, pounding his way to the heavyweight championship of the world—Jack Dempsey, the Manassa Mauler. And Dempsey, for my money, was the greatest champion the world has ever seen. It is true that Gene Tunney, after literary dalliance with Bernard Shaw, took the crown away from Dempsey, but all champions have to topple from their thrones, and before that sad ending Dempsey had been the most savage and ruthless killer of them all.

You may ask how Dempsey would have shaped against those two great negro fighters, Jack Johnson and Joe Louis. Your guess is as good as mine, but I say he would have whipped them, if he could have fought them in his prime. Even Jack Johnson, that prodigiously strong and crafty fighter—Dempsey, I believe, would have beaten him by sheer ferocity, by the animal savagery of his attack.

I met Dempsey when he had just established himself on top of the heap. He was dark, swarthy and blue-chinned, but not a particularly big man. There was weight in his shoulders, though, and speed in his tapering legs, and he would sway lightly on the balls of his feet as he spoke to you.

He was quiet, almost gentle, but his eyes, under craggy brows, his eyes were intense and pebble-hard.

Perhaps you saw him fight Carpentier, that elegant and remarkable Frenchman, for the championship of the world. Carpentier, it is true, was only a light-heavyweight—he won the world title in that division—but he had a crushing right-hand punch, the punch which put our Joe Beckett to sleep while spectators were still settling themselves in their seats.

Carpentier knew that to beat Dempsey he had to land that punch

and land it early.   He did land it, exactly as he and his manager,
Descamps, had planned, a fearful crack to Dempsey's jaw.   He broke
his hand in doing so, and Dempsey rocked back on his heels, shook
his head, and came charging in like an angry bear to pound Carpentier
to defeat.

Those were great days in the boxing world.   There was the tragedy
of Carpentier's defeat by Battling Siki, an unknown negro whose
pleasure it was to parade through the streets of Paris leading a lion
on a chain.   There was the ice-cold and undefeated Gene Tunney, who
regarded boxing as an intellectual exercise.

There were middleweights like Harry Greb, Tiger Flowers and the
great Mickey Walker, and, in Britain, Ted (Kid) Lewis, Tommy
Milligan and Len Harvey.   Yes, without a doubt there were champions in the 1920 ring, champions who would, in my view, sweep the
crowns off the heads of those who wear them now.

It was not only in boxing that the great performers were to be
found.   Everywhere in sport there were personality and achievement.
Perhaps the times were more propitious, and men could find in their
sport more readily the zest and incentive so necessary to high performance.   We had, it appeared, just won the great war to end all wars.
Long years of untroubled prosperity and peace, we assumed, lay
ahead of us.   In that mental atmosphere men could enjoy themselves
and plunge wholeheartedly into their games.

We had not, moreover, reached the noisy and nauseating age of
ballyhoo in sport.   Games, it is true, were reported and reported fully,
but with lingering vestiges of perspective and responsibility.   Writers
were interested in the game rather than the headline and the news
story.   The pools and television had not arrived.   The radio com-
mentator was only hesitantly learning his trade.   The result of a
football match with a continental team was not yet likely to alarm
the Foreign Office and affect national prestige.   We still clung, in fact,
to the quaint notion that games—even first-class games—were
primarily intended to be enjoyed.

Who, for instance, could watch batsmen like Jack Hobbs and Frank
Woolley without sharing their obvious delight in their skill?   In 1925
Hobbs scored sixteen centuries, and although I was not fortunate
enough to see all those innings, I'll warrant that each one of them
bore the unmistakable hall-mark of the creative artist at work, rather
than the niggling, careful and average-conscious plodder.   And what an
incomparable artist Hobbs was!   I would rather watch him make
twenty runs against the spinners on a lively wicket with that perfect

Sport wore a smile in the 'Twenties. *Right:* The Prince of Wales and his brother, then the Duke of York, at a polo tournament in 1921. *Below:* the ever-smiling Georges Carpentier

What a genial smile spread across that wide mouth of Jack Hobbs when he scored his sixteenth century of the season in 1925! And what flags and flowers enveloped Gertrude Ederle as she kissed her mother on her return to New York after swimming the Channel—the first woman to do so, 1926. (*Picture Post Library*)

Three of the great creative artists of cricket. A. P. F. Chapman taking an uncatchable catch in the gully; Frank Woolley stroking the ball away from his stumps with lazy grace; and Jack Hobbs completing an elegant hook to the square leg boundary

footwork and balance of his than sit through a double century by Bradman.

And Frank Woolley—where are adequate superlatives to describe his majesty and power? Woolley slashing a fast bowler through the covers, or picking a bumper off his eyebrows with a contemptuous bang or using his great height and reach to go to the pitch of the ball and drive it sizzling to the boundary, and then, when the despairing bowler shortened his length, cutting him square or hooking him with savage force and exquisite grace.

There were other great cricketers in the 'Twenties—Roy Kilner of Yorkshire, Patsy Hendren, Wilfred Rhodes, Philip Mead, Cecil Parkin, Sutcliffe, Tate and Larwood, and Hammond was beginning his wonderful career.

The crop of amateurs also was outstanding. I had the privilege—or the misfortune—in the 1920 Freshman's match at Oxford—of facing the bowling of G. T. S. Stevens and R. H. Bettington. It was no real consolation to me when later in the season I saw Bettington bowl Hobbs round his legs. Stevens was a great all-rounder who played for the Gentlemen at Lords while he was still at school.

The Universities were rich in outstanding players during the 'Twenties. There was D. R. Jardine, for example, most dour of captains and immaculate of batsmen, and A. P. F. Chapman, who in his youthful prime embodied for me the true spirit of cricket. What zest he brought to the game and how glorious he was to watch when he was making runs, and what catches he took close to the wicket in his enormous hands!

Then there were the Ashtons, and C. S. Marriott, who snapped his fingers like a pistol shot as he spun the ball at you, and L. P. Hedges of Tonbridge, with a cover drive like Wally Hammond's. Then R. W. V. Robins appeared at Cambridge, ready to make all the runs and bowl or catch everybody out, and K. S. Duleepsinhji, most exquisite of batsmen, who told me that he did not need to watch the bowler's hand since he could see the ball spinning in the air, and Arthur Gilligan, ready to bowl his heart out on the hottest summer day.

But there were other amateurs—D. J. Knight of Surrey, P. G. H. Fender, the shrewdest captain of them all, Lionel Tennyson, who made seventy runs against the Australians with one hand, A. W. Carr of Notts, J. C. White and V. W. C. Jupp, to name but a few of the great men who delighted us in those vintage years. Is it merely nostalgia which makes me think that cricket in the 'Twenties had a fire and a glory about it which somehow are lacking today?

Perhaps the passage of time has slightly distorted my perspective on cricket, but about Rugby football I am prepared to be more positive. The standard of Rugby football, in my opinion, was higher in the 'Twenties than it is now. Collectively and individually, the quality of play was better. I believe the England team, which included such men as W. W. Wakefield, R. Cove-Smith, Tom Voyce, W. J. A. Davies and C. A. Kershaw, would have handsomely beaten the Springboks who toured here so victoriously last season.

The forwards of that period were tremendous. What is more, they were scrummaging forwards. They would use the wheel and the straight shove to force the defence out of position. They packed solidly and worked cohesively in the tight. They practised the fundamental arts of forward play and created opportunities and openings for their backs.

W. W. Wakefield—there was a forward for you! Thirteen stone of bone and muscle, phenomenally strong and fast as a wing three-quarter. And G. S. Conway, who looked rather slight, but was made of whip-cord and could dribble like Stanley Matthews. Tom Voyce, the fair-haired giant from Gloucester, always in the thick of the fight, hurling himself over to score with three men clinging round his neck; Cove-Smith, solid as a tree-trunk, impervious to knocks or kicks; Sam Tucker of Bristol, with his great shoulders and his bull-neck, buckling up the opposing front row as he hooked for the ball.

They were forwards indeed, and England had plenty more like them in those fruitful years, while Scotland could produce the magnificent J. M. Bannerman, and the Irish pack was galvanized by that remarkable player W. F. (Horsey) Browne.

Then look at the players behind the scrummage in the 'Twenties. First the half-backs, beginning with that outstanding pair, Davies and Kershaw. These two were the greatest pair of half-backs I have ever seen or ever expect to see, and Kershaw was by no means the junior partner. It was Kershaw's bullet-like pass from the scrummage which gave Davies the extra second and yard or two in which to manoeuvre, and it was Kershaw's great strength and nimbleness which enabled him to stop opposing forwards or nip through near the scrum to score on his own.

His understanding with Davies was perfect, and as for Davies, when he received the ball, his mind worked with lightning speed. He would slip through half a gap like an eel, or draw his man and time his pass exquisitely, or nurse his forwards at critical moments with long touch-finders, or drop a goal as coolly as if practising at a punt-about.

There were other great half-backs in the 'Twenties—J. B. Nelson and H. Waddell of Scotland, almost as dangerous as their English counterparts—Wick Powell of Wales, with that astonishing reverse pass of his, and little Arthur Young, most unorthodox of scrum-halves, who would go diving and slithering under the threshing arms of would-be tacklers until he broke clear away.

Then among the three-quarters the peerless C. N. Lowe was still playing, still coming across the field to tackle the man on the opposite wing; Ian Smith, the Flying Scotsman; G. P. S. Macpherson, that most brilliant centre; G. V. Stephenson of Ireland with his cast-iron defence; Eddie Myers, running straight as a die; L. J. Corbett passing to A. M. Smallwood through his legs, and Smallwood dropping a goal against France from the touch-line. And at full-back such players as Barry Cumberlege, Dan Drysdale and Ernie Crawford.

This is an impressive list of names, but I put them down just as they appear in the memory. Many more could be added to their gallant company. They were without question great years, the 'Twenties, for the great game of Rugby football.

For other games too they were propitious. I remember in 1920 seeing the rubicund C. J. H. Tolley towed in triumph through the streets of Oxford, when he returned to his studies after beating J. Gardiner of U.S.A. in the final of the Amateur Golf Championship. And playing with him in the Oxford side that year was that beautiful stylist Roger Wethered, who in 1921 tied with Jock Hutchison of America for first place in the Open and lost the play-off through treading on his ball and forfeiting the vital stroke. And in the 1923 Walker Cup match Tolley and Wethered overwhelmed Ouimet and Sweetser of America by 6 and 5 at St. Andrews, and made us feel that perhaps our American friends were not quite as formidable as they looked.

We know now that this was indeed wishful thinking, and we might have guessed it when a young man called R. T. (Bobby) Jones appeared in the American team. In the 1926 Walker Cup match Bobby Jones beat Cyril Tolley by the convincing margin of 12 and 11 and went on to win the Open Championship. No one was particularly surprised, for in the Southern qualifying competition for the Open at Sunningdale Jones had two rounds of 66 and 68. The par score for the 6,472 yards course was 72. Bobby Jones was a wonderful player— the greatest who ever lived, many good judges would say—and in 1930 he won within five months the four championships—the British and American Amateur, and Open. He hit the ball with a fluent, easy, compact swing, which made the game look deceptively easy, but he found that the strain of championship play upset his digestion, and he lived largely on charcoal biscuits and milk.

There were, as there always are, some remarkable golfers in America at that time, men like Walter Hagen, Leo Diegel, Gene Sarazen and Macdonald Smith, and we had some fine players in Great Britain. There was the mercurial George Duncan, who beat Walter Hagen in the 1929 Ryder Cup match by 10 and 8 and helped Britain to win by seven matches to five.   Then there was Archie Compston, that colourful character, and the burly Ted Ray, with his pipe and his niblick, and Henry Cotton on his way to fame as one of the world's finest golfers.

In the 'Twenties, too, among the ladies we had the reign of Joyce Wethered, the greatest lady player of them all, not excluding that fabulous American performer, Babe Zaharias.   Joyce Wethered won the English championship from the redoubtable Miss Cecil Leitch in 1920, and held it without serious difficulty until 1925.   The smallest margin by which she won the final was 7 and 6, and in 1921 she crushed the unfortunate Mrs. Mudford by 13 and 11.

If golf flourished in the 'Twenties, so did lawn tennis.   There was that tremendous American W. T. Tilden.   I remember seeing him defeat G. L. Patterson in 1920, and crashing home his cannon-ball service to beat B. I. C. Norton in 1921 after he had lost the first two sets.   Tilden did not triumph by the streamlined efficiency, the smooth, rhythmic stroke production of the modern champion, but he gave an impression of sheer savage power which suggested that he would blow his opponent off the court.

Then there were those four extraordinary Frenchmen—Borotra, the Bounding Basque, Lacoste, Cochet and Brugnon, who from 1924 to 1930 virtually monopolized the men's singles.

And it was in 1919 that the tranquillity of a quiet South Kensington hotel where I was staying was somewhat disturbed by a volatile party of visitors from France.   There was a rather plain but extremely vivacious young lady with her parents.   Her name was Suzanne Lenglen, and she shook the lawn tennis world by beating Mrs. Lambert Chambers to win the ladies' singles title, a title which she held until 1926.

Mlle Lenglen was a beautiful player who revolutionized the women's game by bringing to it a new daring and speed in attack, and she was succeeded by that remarkable American, 'little poker-face' Helen Wills, who won the title eight times between the wars.

Lawn tennis, then, was healthy enough in the 'Twenties, and real

The great ones of golf. *Above:* Cyril Tolley with Miss Joyce Wethered, 1925. *Right:* Walter Hagen preparing for the British Open Championship, 1924. *Below:* three generations of the Bobby Jones family welcome the conquering hero on his return to New York

Three of the Immortals of Sport: Suzanne Lenglen, Jack Dempsey, W. W. Wakefield (*Picture Post Library*)

tennis, its distinguished progenitor, was dominated by the great E. M. Baerlein, who won the M.C.C. Gold Racket every year between 1921 and 1929, and the professionals G. F. Covey and Pierre Etchebaster.

And what of athletics? After the war, with its tragic waste of youth, we might have expected our stock to be low, but far from it. Bevil Rudd was up at Oxford, and in 1920 he won the 400 metres in the Olympic Games at Antwerp. In that same year A. G. Hill of Great Britain won both the 800 and the 1,500 metres, P. Hodge the 3,000 metres steeplechase and Great Britain the 1,600 metres relay.

Then came those great Cambridge athletes Guy Butler, Harold Abrahams and D. G. A. Lowe. In the 1924 Games in Paris, Abrahams won the 100 metres, Liddell the 400 metres, and Lowe the 800 metres, which he won again in 1928 at Amsterdam.

At that period there were other fine runners in plenty—men like W. R. Milligan, E. P. Mountain, H. B. Stallard and W. R. Seagrove, and hurdlers of outstanding quality like Lord Burghley, G. C. Weightman and R. M. N. Tisdall.

It is clear that athletics flourished in the 'Twenties; it is indeed difficult to think of any branch of sport which did not produce superb performers. Billiards, for example, was extremely popular—snooker had not then come to the fore—and such remarkable exponents as Tom Newman, with his jutting jaw right down to the cue, Willie Smith, Melbourne Inman, most dour of fighters, J. Reece and H. W. Stevenson drew large crowds whenever they played.

Miss Gertude Ederle in 1926 was the first woman to swim the Channel, crossing from Cap Grisnez to Dover in 14 hours 34 minutes. And, between 1920 and 1930, Oxford won the Boat Race once.

Taking it by and large, therefore, the 'Twenties were crowded and splendid years in sport. They were years, moreover, when sport still retained a light-hearted element, a flavour of enjoyment, a suggestion of a smile. The smile is fading now, and the sports columnist sits most severely in judgment, thundering his wrathful condemnation of players and officials who fail to give spectators value for money. Sport and box-office are synonymous. Players are entertainers subject to the crack of the public whip.

Maybe this is a good thing. I do not happen to think so, but then, in sport I am a reactionary. I look back wistfully to the days when there was less publicity but more pleasure in sport. To the 'Twenties, in short—to the golden age of my youth.

N

The Golden Age of Jazz

by HUMPHREY LYTTELTON

JAZZ history has a most convenient habit of arranging itself into decades. Starting from the half-true assumpton that jazz began in the neighbourhood of 1900, it is quite easy for the glib historian to mark off the development of the music into periods of ten years, with a portmanteau chapter-heading—the Swing Age, the Classic Period, and so on—for each one. My title for this short essay on jazz in the 'Twenties is ready-made. The 'Golden Age' tag has been handed down by previous generations of chroniclers, and is generally accepted as being appropriate to the period. I have a suspicion that it was first applied early in the 'Thirties in a moment of bitter reaction against Swing Music ; jazz lovers are quick to adopt a 'things-aren't-what-they-used-to-be' philosophy whenever the object of their affections shows a change of mood.

Nowadays, when we stand far enough away from the trees to see the wood in perspective, the tag requires qualification. During the last ten years, a revival of interest in the prototype New Orleans jazz has directed a critical onslaught upon the 'Golden Age,' and most of the accepted doctrines of the period have been either modified or completely reversed. In order to give a true picture of the development of jazz in the 'Twenties the essayist must combine two themes—the True Golden Age, only lately discovered, and the Pinchbeck age which our precedessors took for gold. For, as I will show, jazz made its first world-wide appearance backwards, and standing on its head. The reason for this lies in the relationship between the people's music from New Orleans and popular music in general. In referring to jazz as people's music, I am not toe-ing a party line, but stating a plain fact.

Seen against the vast back-cloth of American music, the beginnings of jazz must seem to the layman to be unbelievably trivial. They can be reduced without too drastic simplification to a single circumstance. New Orleans in the 'Eighties and 'Nineties was a gay city which demanded music to accompany its festive moments. High Society had its trained bands and orchestras. Low Life had nothing. So Low Life took the law into its own hands and provided music for itself. Untaught musicians, both black and white, provided rough and ready music for the parades, picnics, dances—and funerals—which were part of the

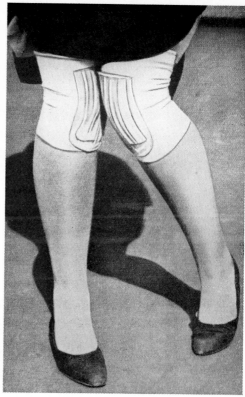

Was there some profound significance in the vogue for masks in the 'Twenties? The Greenwich Folly girl above wears a mask by Benda (1921). Lauri Devine, surrounded by Oliver Messel masks, sings 'Dance, Little Lady' in Noel Coward's 'This Year of Grace' at the London Pavilion, 1928. For less graceful executants was devised the Charleston Knee-cap (*Picture Post Library*)

JELLY ROLL MORTON
(*Jazz Journal photo*)

life of the city. The fact that this music was untutored would not by itself have resulted in jazz. But the Negro musicians from the poor, uptown quarter differed from the whites in two important respects. They were not hamstrung by an ill-digested academic tradition ; and they had behind them a tradition of their own which was improvisational in character, stretching back through plantation songs, spirituals and slave chants to the drums of Africa. It was the application of this vocal and rhythmic tradition to the raw materials of popular music which produced the jazz language. The Negro improviser in New Orleans carried over into his playing many of the idiosyncrasies of the Afro-American singing style—a thick, almost husky tone, a pronounced vibrato, and a habit of striking certain notes in the scale off-pitch. The use of just one of these digressions from conventional, academic usage would cost a straight symphony or dance man his job within five minutes.

It is important to emphasize here that New Orleans jazz was not the first syncopated dance music to find its way into the musical life of America. Long before it had made any mark outside its native city, there were syncopated songs and dances to be heard all over the country in the 'coon' and minstrel entertainments. By the publication in 1897 of two pieces, Tom Turpin's 'Harlem Rag' and the classic cake-walk 'At a Georgia Camp Meeting' by Kerry Mills, syncopation was firmly established in American popular music. It is a fallacy that the first time the American Negro put an instrument to his lips, jazz music came pouring out. Throughout the development of ragtime into what we now call straight dance music, Negroes with the talent and opportunity to learn to read and write 'music' were contributing their share, in conventional fashion, and there is no evidence that their style differed much from that of their colleagues in the white bands.

During the second decade of the century, America went dance crazy, and the emphasis in popular music shifted from the song to the dance. The mad, hectic era following the First World War has been restrospectively dubbed the Jazz Age. This is misleading, because jazz in the true sense was neither responsible for, nor inspired by, the post-war mood. The Roaring 'Twenties would have roared just as loudly had jazz music never emerged from New Orleans, for the dance music industry was by then a thriving concern, and could doubtless have continued to pour forth its stream of 'hits' without any assistance from jazz.

What happened, however, was that in 1917 the city authorities in New Orleans closed the Storyville brothel district, and the music which had hitherto been concentrated within the space of a few blocks in a single city, spilled out all over the world.   By 1919 it had reached as far as London, which received its first inoculation at the hands of the Original Dixieland Jazz Band.   But, of all the towns and cities which received it, only two are of direct importance to its development through the 'twenties—Chicago, the natural up-river terminus, and New York, the capital of the Entertainment World.

In Chicago jazz established a home from home.   The tough, slap-happy mood of gangsterdom found in it a sympathetic accompaniment. And furthermore, the city South Side housed a large Negro population which had moved up from the Mississipi valley to find work in the factories, and which knew and understood the music of the Blues from which jazz had sprung.   By 1920 many of the most renowned New Orleans men were living and working in Chicago, passing on the secret of their music to the young local musicians who came to hear them, and contributing to what was discovered, twenty years later, to have been a very rich period of New Orleans music.

The research into early jazz which has taken place over the last ten years has raised doubts about the 'purity' of the music which was first recorded in Chicago.   One school of thought asserts that, by the time King Oliver and his Creole Jazz Band cut the first Negro jazz records, there had already been a decline under the baleful influence of com-mercial dance music.   The claim is supported by the musical evidence of a handful of old-timers who have never left the southern city, and who are therefore supposed to reflect the true, untainted spirit of old New Orleans.   It is true that the recently recorded music of Bunk Johnson, George Lewis, Kid Rena and the rest is simpler and rougher than the jazz recorded in Chicago during the 'Twenties ; but it is a rash critic who lays down the work of old and unpractised men as a standard for all time.

Without doubt, at some period in its development, jazz music acquired a sense of form and craftsmanship which it lacked in its primitive stages.   There is good evidence to show that this maturing process took place long before the Chicago period ; it was certainly maintained until well into the middle of it.   The leading figures in recorded Chicago jazz during the 'Twenties—King Oliver, Johnny Dodds, Louis Armstrong, Jelly Roll Morton—were men who developed and organized the jazz language along personal lines.   In most instances there was no question of commercialism.   Their records were made for a Negro market which required no concessions, and the custom of recruiting their bands from New Orleans men is proof enough of the care which they took in preserving the character of their music. The jazz of King Oliver may have been more advanced than that of Buddy Bolden, but there is no reason for thinking that it was less pure.

The whole question of 'purity' in jazz is one which very easily topples over into absurdity. It is difficult to argue that any music can be pure which acknowledges influences from Africa, Spain, France, England, and America. I have suggested already that jazz is more of a musical language than a complete music in itself. And as such it is capable of infinite extension and variation. When Louis Armstrong in his early Hot Five recordings (1926–28) expanded the traditional improvised break into a full length virtuoso chorus, he was merely stretching part of the jazz idiom to suit his own temperament. Likewise, Jelly Roll Morton's custom of transcribing his piano solos for New Orleans bands was a perfectly legitimate device wherein no precious 'purity' was sacrificed. On the other hand, it can be claimed that, when musicians without understanding of the jazz language started to prune away its characteristic features, and to replace them with great chunks of non-jazz material, the result was a hybrid which can fairly be called impure   And that is just what happened when jazz reached New York.

As early as 1916 two little groups from New Orleans, the Original Creole Band (under Freddie Keppard) and the Original Dixieland Band, had made a sensation on Broadway. New Orleans jazz had come to town. And its subsequent fate in the Big City holds the secret of the misconception which underlies the Golden Age Legend. New York was the headquarters of show-business, and the whole musical life of the city was devoted to the service of a great industry. When jazz hit Broadway it made an immediate appeal, not as music, but as a stunt. To borrow from the contemporary jargon of Tin Pan Alley, it had a gimmick. And Broadway was quick to exploit it. Soon every musician who had strength in his arm or breath in his lungs was clattering and blasting away in crude imitation of the men from the South. The fearful din which resulted inevitably brought on a reaction, and when the Original Dixieland Jazz Band returned to New York after triumph in England, they soon found that their magic had gone. The stolid tradition of straight dance-music, with its strict code of musical etiquette, had asserted itself in their absence, and 'ear-music' was beyond the pale.

The violent reaction which followed the pseudo-jazz craze in New York is significant to our theme, because it set up a prevailing atmosphere against New Orleans jazz which kept the music at bay through-out the decade. After the initial success of the Creole Band and the Original Dixielanders, New York set its face against this unruly music and refused to accept it unless it was dressed up in the decent clothing of 'musicianship.' Paul Whiteman, a big man with a big band, set the style with his symphonic jazz, a product which was innocent of the slightest taint of real jazz music. In the recording studios a group of musicians who had fallen for the Dixieland style and had developed a polite variation of it succeeded in cornering the recording market for 'hot' jazz. The partnership of Red Nichols and Miff Mole, which led this little clique, heads the Pinchbeck Age roll-of-honour. The former was a competent musician with a flair for imitation and a highly developed business sense, while the latter aroused the admiration of fellow-musicians with his formidable trombone technique. Neither of them ever got close to the heart of jazz. The drawing-room music which they and their various groups recorded so prolifically cuts an elegant but feeble figure beside the New Orleans original.

In Harlem, where one might have expected some sort of natural musical activity corresponding to that of the Negro districts in New Orleans and Chicago, show-business also had a crippling hold. For Harlem was a show-place for sightseers, and the large and flashy Negro bands were too busy providing 'Negroid' music for tourist consumption to worry about anything else. Nevertheless, the music of the Original Creole Band had made a deeper impression on Harlem than on Broad-way, and had started a school of hot playing which was certainly superior to the refined effusions of Whiteman and Nichols. This was further boosted by the influence of New Orleans men who joined the big Harlem bands. In 1924, Louis Armstrong spent several months in Fletcher Henderson's Orchestra, and when he sickened of the plati-tudinous dance music which he had to play, and returned to Chicago, he left his mark on the style of the band. Listening to one of the records which Armstrong made with the Henderson Orchestra, one receives a vivid impression of the fundamental difference in language between New Orleans jazz and popular dance music. Armstrong's occasional solos leap out of the wax with all the vitality of a living music, while, of the rest, nothing is left but a collection of out-dated mannerisms. By the late 'Twenties Negro bands such as Henderson's, Luis Russell's and Duke Ellington's (all bolstered up with New Orleans men) had evolved a synthesis of jazz and dance music which retained the language of the former to a very large extent. Ten years later they called it Swing Music and it had a great vogue. But throughout the

Vintage jazz bands: Brownlee's Orchestra of New Orleans, and (*below*) King Oliver's Creole Band. (*Jazz Journal photos*)

Protagonists in the battle of Sacred and Profane—Jazz and Swing. Duke Ellington and Louis Armstrong

'Twenties it was just Harlem jazz, lapped up by the tourist and Negro population, but offering no serious competition to the white orchestras on Broadway, to whom colour discrimination gave a head start.

As a general rule, then, we can say that throughout the 'Twenties jazz was appreciated in New York in inverse proportion to its authenticity. Even if we rule the pretentious concert-jazz of Paul Whiteman out of court altogether, we are still left with the fact that Red Nichols and his colleagues represented to the New Yorker the ultimate in 'modern hot style.' In itself, this reversal of values would have had very little effect on the course of jazz history but for one important and, for good jazz, disastrous fact. It was New York, and not Chicago, which was the nerve-centre of world-wide show business. And New York in the 'Twenties held the position in relation to jazz which Paris holds today in relation to feminine fashion. Largely through the medium of the record companies, whose largest studios were, of course, in New York, the city established itself as the arbiter of taste.

The effect of this upon the history of jazz appreciation in this country, to take one example, was quite devastating. Every phase of New York's complex reaction to jazz music was reflected in England, from the original jazz craze onwards. Jack Hylton became London's Paul Whiteman, and the imitations, by his 'Jazz Band,' of Paul Whiteman's impressions of the Original Dixieland Band's version of the Negro music of New Orleans can still be found in the junk record piles outside the premises of second-hand dealers. Anti-jazz reaction in New York was echoed in London, and in its issue of November 1927 the *Melody Maker,* mouthpiece of the British dance music profession, had occasion to reprimand the Columbia Record Company for using the word 'Jazz' in its publicity material.

> 'I wonder if the Columbia record people know what this word conveys to musicians,' asked the record-reviewer, 'Needlepoint.' 'If not, let me hasten to enlighten them by saying that it signifies everything that is bad and everything that is old-fashioned. It is a word of sarcasm.'

The theme that jazz was old-fashioned runs through all the *Melody Maker* reviews of the period. It was based, with some justification, on the fourth-hand music which had been accepted as jazz in the early 'Twenties. But it led poor 'Needlepoint' into some unfortunate judgments. When a few recordings by Jelly Roll Morton trickled out into the English catalogues, they sounded to his untutored ear to be near enough to the music of the 'jazz craze' for him to pan them as being out of date. From our present-day vantage point, we can recognize that Morton's 'Blackbottom Stomp' was, even for 1927, extremely advanced New Orleans jazz, which bears as much relation to the stilted derivatives of 'Dixieland' as a Grecian vase to a cloche hat.

We need not dwell upon the contemporary attitude to Negro performers betrayed by such *Melody Maker* comments as 'the nigger has a heart as big as his great woolly head,' beyond saying that it served as a further barrier to the acceptance of real jazz. A craving for respectability is one of the British dance-band musician's prevailing characteristics, and his efforts to disassociate himself from what he called 'coon' music flung him straight into the arms of Red Nichols, whose reputation grew to vast proportions. By the middle of the decade, Nichols had himself fallen under the spell of a young cornet-player who had come to New York with the Wolverine Orchestra from Chicago. The band was a failure, but Bix Beiderbecke emerged from it to take the leadership in the white jazz field. Although it is almost heresy to say it, Beiderbecke's example strengthened the anti-jazz forces. His own clear-cut melodic style was, in itself, a striking concoction of jazz and straight ingredients, highly enjoyable and commendable in isolation, but disastrous when accepted and imitated as being the real thing. Red Nichols and his associates were dazzled by Bix, and their music from 1925 onwards proclaims his influence from every bar. But as we have seen already, what New York thought at a given time was conveyed, through the sluggish channels of the gramophone industry, to the British critical mind two or three years later. And while Red Nichols was devoting himself to the slavish imitation of Bix's mannerisms, 'Needlepoint' was delivering the following judgment in the *Melody Maker* of September, 1927 : —

'In Riverboat Shuffle' and 'Ostrich Walk' . . . the laurels must go to Bix Bidlebeck, the trumpet player, who loses nothing when compared to the great Red Nichols.'

It is not my intention to set up the *Melody Maker* reviewer of the time as an Aunt Sally. It is difficult to see how, under the circumstances, anybody could have approached much nearer to the heart of jazz when the channels of information were controlled and directed by New York. Indeed, but for the fact that the big record companies of the day decided to cash in on an unexploited section of the public by issuing a series of 'Race' records for Negro consumption only, it is probable that the real jazz in Chicago would have remained in oblivion to this day. By the end of the 'Twenties the link with New Orleans had begun to wear thin, and one by one, the exiles succumbed to the demands of show-business. By 1926, King Oliver's New Orleans Band had been succeeded by a large orchestra in the Harlem pattern, and Louis Armstrong, while clinging to the hometown style in the recording-studios, was beginning to develop the virtuoso technique which was to bring him world-wide fame. Consistent with the topsy-turvy pattern of jazz appreciation in the 'Twenties, Armstrong's big-band work in the service of show-business completely overshadowed his finest playing in the New Orleans tradition. The now classic Hot Five recordings, made in Chicago for the Okeh Race lists, only found their way into the general catalogues by virtue of his popularity in the Swing field.

As the 'Twenties were drawing their last gasp, there began a movement away from the New York white school towards Negro jazz. But by then New Orleans music was in total eclipse, and the men of Harlem took the bows. It was not until ten years later that there began a determined attempt to unravel the threads of gold and pinchbeck. For most jazz lovers the world over, the New Orleans Revival was not so much a revival as a revelation. It brought to light the treasury of jazz music which had been locked away in the obscure 'Race' record lists, and established in a position of due importance the musicians— many of them now dead—who were responsible for forging a real Golden Age of Jazz. How far that age extended back before the invention of the gramophone we can only guess. As for the future— who knows? Events may be forthcoming which will make a 'Needle-point' out of me.

The Age of Release

by C. E. M. JOAD

LOOKING back on the 'Twenties, I recall it as pre-eminently an age of release and, predominantly, of intellectual release. This was largely the outcome of the work of Shaw and Wells. Born into the later Victorian Age, these great men had grown up into a world hedged about with conventions. Growing up in this world was like walking down a gallery lined with lay figures, the figures of Victorian respectability, figures of gentlemanliness and ladylikeness, of church-going and of the clothes proper to church-going, figures of patriotism and figures of duty. . . . Through the ribs of these figures they passed the rapiers of their wit; there trickled out some sawdust and a little bran and, lo and behold, the figures were no more.

The Dead March in the *Eroica Symphony* goes on for what seems a very long time; gloomier and more sombre grows the music, slower and slower the pace, as one by one the lights of hope and zest and joy go out. It is all very oppressive, and by the end of the movement one is feeling very low indeed. Into this atmosphere of oppressive gloom there breaks suddenly the dancing measure of the scherzo, and in an instant all is changed. It is exactly as if a pretty housemaid had come tripping into a long-shut-up-room, heavy with hangings, shrouded in dust sheets, cluttered with furniture. She opens the windows, fling back the shutters and lets in the air and the sweet, fresh smells of spring. Morning bird-song is heard through the open windows, the room is alive with sunlight and, as she dusts the furniture, motes dance in its beams.

It was exactly with this same effect that Shaw and Wells burst into the long-closed room of Victorian middle-class respectability. They were pre-eminently liberators, and they liberated a generation. But just as we were about to enjoy the freedoms that they had won, the war closed down on us and for five years more our liberation was held up. When at last the war came to an end, it was as if a great dam had been removed and the waters of the spirit flowed free and unconfined. The spirit, in fact, went on holiday.

The holiday spirit was expressed in a revolt against the Victorians, a revolt typified in literature by the work of Lytton Strachey and Aldous Huxley. Strachey took the great figures of Victorian solemnity

THE AGE OF RELEASE—and some of the liberators.
Above, right: Augustus John and Jacob Epstein. *Below:*
Shaw, Belloc and Chesterton after the famous Shaw-
Chesterton debate. (Photos by Dorien Leigh, Alvin Langdon
Coburn and *Picture Post Library*)

Of course we weren't *all* 'highbrows'—as they began to call us—then. A lot of people read the novels on the left, a lot of people went to see the Co-optimists (*below*), and, of course, *everyone* saw Rudolph Valentino as 'The Sheik' (*Picturegoer* photograph)

and showed us their littleness. Huxley showed us our own. If one were to select a single book as typical of the period, it would be *Antic Hay*. In this book Gumbril, a young master in a preparatory school, finds his hindquarters galled by the discomforts of the hard seat in chapel on which he must sit to endure the long services. Unable to take a cushion into chapel, he conceives the notion of air-inflated trousers. He designs them, comes to London, takes out a patent, acquires wealth, becomes a man-about-town, pursues women, goes to concerts. . . . The book is in effect a hilariously derisive picture of Bohemian life in London in the early 'Twenties.

Its freedoms were a little startling even to those who had been groomed for freedom by Shaw and Wells. This was the age in which little boys ran after bearded gentlemen in the street with yells of 'beaver,' and Gumbril buys and dons a beard as a symptom of virility. But the real 'beaver' he-man is Coleman. 'Christ-like in my behaviour,' he chants as he bursts into a restaurant, 'like every good believer, I imitate the Saviour and cultivate a beaver.'

The book ends on a note of disillusion as Gumbril and Mrs Viveash, devotees of pleasure, drive round the West End in a taxi seeking the wherewithal to be amused. Having squeezed the orange of their customary friends and pleasures, they are profoundly bored and go from acquaintance to acquaintance, from night-club to night-club in quest of fresh sensation, finally fetching up in a laboratory, to watch the physiologist Shearwater pedalling a stationary bicycle in an enclosed glass cubicle in order to find out how much sweat the human frame secretes as a result of a given expenditure of effort. The burthen of *Antic Hay*, if so light-hearted a book can be said to have a burthen, is that no one thing is better than any other thing, that nothing in itself is true, nothing in itself good, that nothing, therefore, is worth believing and there is no object but pleasure. The golden rule is that there is no golden rule. Hence, do what you will and have the courage and ingenuity 'to get away' with it. . . .

Another sort of intellectual release was expressed in the poetry of the time. This was the heyday of the Georgian poets. The conventions and solemnities of the great age of Victorian poetry had been dropped. The new conventions, the obscurity, the involution, the allusiveness of the new era which began with the publication of *The Waste Land*, had still to come. Straightforwardness was the order of the day, as in simple lyrics the poet expressed the moment of ecstasy in love or in the appreciation of nature, particularly the appreciation of nature. W. H. Davies, Ralph Hodgson and Blunden were generally admired, and the deceptive simplicity of W. H. Davies's nature poems,

> *'What is this life, if full of care,*
> *We have no time to stand and stare ?'*

or 'Sweet chance, that led my steps abroad, . . .' caused them to be read wherever intellectuals gathered for week-ends in the country. (The week-end habit, just getting under way, was at once blessed and catered for in the Nonesuch Press's celebrated *Week-end Book*).

The release, secondly, was an emotional release—a release, in particular, from the admonitions of the Victorian conscience. The Victorians envisaged the conscience as a sort of barmaid of the soul, countenancing—since, after all, men are but human—such indulgence of desires as propriety permits ; countenancing them, however, only for a time and up to a point. And then : 'Time's up, gentlemen,' she says, 'no more drinking after 10.30,' and closes the bar. If gentlemen continue to drink after the admonitions of conscience, they get into trouble with the law. In other words, conscience gives them a bad time and remorse follows. Such was the teaching of the Victorians.

But with the coming of the early 'Twenties came also Freud, and the first, fine springtime of psycho-analysis. What psycho-analysis taught was that the part of you which you know about, the part, therefore, that you control or think you control, is not the part that matters. For the control is illusory. The part of us that really guides our steps is unconscious, is, in fact, *'the* unconscious.' 'The unconscious' was conceived and presented by many Freudians as a sort of underground prisoner, a skeleton in the cupboard of the personality, normally kept chained in the dark, but every now and then apt to burst his bonds and break in upon our daylight respectability with horrid groans and atavistic lusts. This view of the matter was set out for the early 'Twenties in a playlet of Aldous Huxley's, *Happy Families,* published in *Limbo,* in which the various elements of the human person, the unconscious, the conscience, the id and so on, are personified as creatures holding conversation together. I can remember this playlet being performed at a private gathering at which the outbursts of the Freudianly primitive Cain—'Oh Nyum, Nyum, ma honey ! Come wid me to Dixieland. . . .'—were received with rapturous hilarity.

This, no doubt, was caricature, though legitimate enough, for Freud often writes as if all the contents of consciousness at any given moment consisted of more or less sublimated versions of elements in the unconscious. This applies not only to the emotional and passional elements of our nature, our desires, wishes, aversions and hopes, but also to our beliefs and thoughts. A man's tastes in art or beliefs about religion are, on this view, just as much determined by the trends of his unconscious self as his taste in female beauty or his beliefs about his own character.

Thus consciousness, including such lately-evolved faculties as reason, will and conscience which the Victorians thought of as the mainsprings of our nature, came to be represented as a sort of cork bobbing on the waves of instinct and desire, its movements determined by currents which ran below the surface.

The effect of all this in its practical application upon the morality of the times is easy to imagine. Morality is a structure built on the twin pillars of praise and blame. If you cannot blame a man for doing wrong and give him credit for doing right, morality goes by the board, yet praise and blame are equally illogical where there is no responsibility for the actions which attract the one and provoke the other.

But psycho-analysis affected men's attitude to experience more directly than through the scepticism which it engendered in regard to the traditional, inhibitory morality. To distrust of the old doctrines of prudence and prohibition it added, as a positive doctrine, the obligation to experiment. It said not merely that it is not worth while to deny ourselves to save the soul, but that it is our duty to spend the soul. Psycho-analysis was responsible, in other words, for a positive creed of self-expression. To thwart an instinctive drive, to stifle an unconscious desire is, Freud taught, to injure the personality at its very root. Nobody had shown more conclusively than he how much of the hysteria, the neurosis and the vague self-dissatisfaction of modern life is due to the repression of natural desires in youth. And not only hysteria and neurosis, but the Puritanism which sees in prohibition the whole duty of man, and equates virtue with self-denial.

As a result, many young people came to regard self-expression as a primary duty and to count repression as, at least, in theory, a sin. Where everything is uncertain, the doctrine of let's eat, drink and be merry for tomorrow we die, at once concrete and definite, was eagerly embraced. Such an attitude, whatever it might mean for a mature sage, involved for the youth of the early 'Twenties a contemptuous abandonment of those restraints which the nineteenth century pretentiously termed its 'morals.' Hadn't death, after all, for most of us, just been miraculously escaped?

The waters of psychology flowed into literature. They found expression in the determination to capture the exact moment of experience in all its fullness without any necessary regard to past moments or to the future. Where the Victorians had presented a group of characters in inter-relation, and the Edwardians and early Georgians had concentrated on the life of some one person (in the novels, for example, of Gilbert Cannan, J. D. Beresford or Hugh Walpole), the writers of the 'Twenties embarked upon an attempt to describe a day, an hour, even a minute, in all its concrete fullness.

Virginia Woolf was at once the exponent and the protagonist of this method. In a passage from a book of literary essays entitled *The Common Reader*, some of which had previously appeared in contemporary periodicals, she bids us 'examine for a moment an ordinary mind on an ordinary day. The mind receives a myriad impressions—trivial, fantastic, evanescent or engraved with the sharpness of steel. From all sides they come, an incessant shower of innumerable atoms. . . .' 'Is it not,' she asks, 'the task of the novelist to convey this varying, this unknown and uncircumscribed spirit, whatever aberration or complexity it may display with as little mixture of the alien and external as possible?' In *Jacob's Room* and *To The Lighthouse,* and in Joyce's *Ulysses,* which is supposed to represent the acts, thoughts and emotions of a single man in a single day, all of which were widely read in the 'Twenties, this principle was practised. Unfortunately, Virginia Woolf was not only widely read but widely imitated. Herself a woman of genius, she produced novels of an exquisite perceptiveness which often succeeded in fulfilling her own ideal and conveying the actual feel and texture of life. But in the hands of her imitators, the method degenerated into a mere fragmentariness, as scenes and incidents without significance succeeded one another without rhyme or reason, the predominant effect being one of portentous dullness.

Two others of the most admired writers of the 'Twenties, Joyce and Lawrence, whose works also bore witness to the pervasiveness of psychology, did not wholly escape this dullness. I give one example from *Ulysses* as illustrating the method at its worst. 'On the boil sure enough ; a plume of steam from the spout. He scalded and rinsed the teapot and put in four full spoons of tea, tilting the kettle then to let the water flow in. Having set it to draw, he took off the kettle and crushed the pan flat on the live coals and watched the lump of butter slide and melt.' But having given my one example, I can't resist the temptation of adding another from the same source. 'Bald deaf Pat brought quite flat Pad ink. Pat sat with ink pen quite flat Pad. Pat took plate dish knife fork. Pat went.' High time, too, the reader thinks.

Above : Voices in the Air. A group of Savoy Hill announcers: *front row:* Rex Palmer, Stuart Hibberd, David Tennant; *back row:* T. Farrar, Eric Dunstan, John Snagge. (*B.B.C. photo*)

Below: Cocktails in the Cellar. Elsa Lanchester entertaining the intelligentzia at her bar in the Cave of Harmony, Seven Dials. (*Picture Post Library*)

Freedom for the Masses—and Emancipation for Women
(*Picture Post Library*)

The 'Twenties were fortunate in the production of literary men of genius, but it may be doubted whether the method which they followed was equally fortunate. In the hands of their successors it led to a dead-end, and stories appeared in regard to which it was equally permissible to wonder why they were ever begun or why, having begun, they ever ended.

Two further releases deserve to be mentioned for the part they played in precipitating what has come to be known as the characteristic mood of the 'Twenties—the release from locality and the release of the dance.

The release from locality was effected by the internal combustion engine. Prior to 1914 cars had been relatively few and were owned only by the relatively rich. Then came the war and people were too busy, harassed or poor to use the car as an instrument of entertainment. Hence it was not until the early 'Twenties that cars became a normal accompaniment of the life of the middle classes. They made an immense difference to the texture of people's lives. In particular, they powerfully assisted the break-up of the family. It was a problem for a middle-class young man of the pre-1914 era interested in a middle-class young woman to know what to do with her or where to take her. Roller-skating was 'all the go,' but a roller-skating rink hardly afforded the desired privacy. The cinemas were in their infancy. The post-1918 young man could, for the first time, take his girl out in a car and so take her away from the shadow of her family's surveillance and the chatter of the neighbour's tongues, take her into the country, take her to the seaside. An enormous loosening up of manners and morals was made possible by this dispersal in space.

The great outbreak of dancing that followed the war was another releasing factor. The pre-1914 dance still tended to be formal. You were invited ; you dressed up ; you were presented with a programme ; you were apt to go with a party ; girls were still supposed to be chaperoned ; and in a rough sort of way it was necessary to know how to dance. You could not, for example, improvise your way through the Lancers. . . .

But now all this was changed. In every suburb dance halls on the model of the Hammersmith Palais de Danse were springing up. To these you need take nothing but a partner and an entrance fee. There were no programmes of set dances and, of course, no chaperones. The enormous simplification of women's dress reduced preparation to the minimum compatible with female vanity. A short skirt that ended, however hideously, at the knees did not demand the formalities or require the tendance of one that trailed about your feet. You could, for example, walk through the streets in it ; while your bobbed hair or Eton crop had at least this advantage—it could be got ready in no time at all.

Above all, 'modern dancing,' as it was called, was something that anybody could do. You shuffled round the room in what a contemporary wit called 'a form of country walking slightly impeded by a member of the opposite sex' and called it a fox-trot. You slid round a little faster and called it a one-step. In spite of the series of new dances which those who made their living out of teaching dancing introduced from time to time, the essentials of the dance grew simpler and simpler. Eventually the fox-trot and the one-step merged into a uniform shuffle which presented no difficulty to anybody. I, at least, in common with thousands of other young men, took to it without preparation or consideration. With cars to take you and your girl away from the restricting influences of the home town, with dance halls waiting to receive you wherever you chose to 'land up,' a great loosening up of the life of the young was inevitable. For the first time young people of both sexes consorted pretty much as they pleased, with the minimum of parental interference. As at once the consequence and the expression of these many releases, the London that I knew surrendered itself to light-hearted merry-making. Never can there have been an age when there were so many 'parties.' . . . .

I have put all this in general terms. Let me try to illustrate by the not untypical case, my own, of a young man living through these expansive years in London.

In the early years of the 'Twenties I happened to be living in Chelsea in one of those ugly houses at the far, unfashionable end of Cheyne Walk, which looked across the river past a celebrated pub. (Was it called The Sun or, perhaps, The World? I can't remember and as Hitler destroyed it with his bombs in the second World War, I shall never know.) On the ground floor lived a successful composer and his wife. The first floor was occupied by our landlady, a pianist with a tubercular spine. She could no longer play the piano but lay on her bed day in and day out, listening for her sins and on occasion overtly objecting to my morning renderings of Beethoven on the pianola just over her head. She would call me down : 'That bridge passage in the fugue'—the last movement of Op. 110—'wants emphasizing with sharp-played, staccato chords. I can't bear to hear it slurred and murdered. You must stop it, you really must!'

Her wants were attended to by the most slatternly, albeit the most faithful of all the London chars I have ever met. This char 'did' for me too for a time, but my interests were so obviously sacrificed to those of my landlady, my pats of butter and bits of bacon so clearly found their way on to her breakfast table, that I presently secured a char of my own, who immediately engaged her colleague in a perpetual internecine warfare. On the second floor I lived, at that time alone. On the third was a journalist and his wife. During the period of my sojourn in the house, the wife of the journalist, who, in the kindness of her heart, used to give me meals, had an 'affair' with the composer. The affair matured. There were nightly comings and goings on the stairs outside my room. Presently the journalist's wife descended the staircase for the last time and was permanently installed on the ground floor with the composer, whose wife went to live with the man next door, a semi-philosopher, semi-mathematician who used to give me incomprehensible explanations of the Theory of Relativity, which was then 'all the go.' The journalist survived, lamenting, on the top floor.

It was with him that I used to go, sometimes in female company, sometimes not, to the parties. These for the most part were 'bottle-parties,' that is to say, you took your own drink with you and handed it over to a pool on arrival. At these parties for the first time in my life I used to get drunk—the first and also the last, since before real happiness set in I was habitually sick, a circumstance which so disgusted me (and everyone else) that after a time I abandoned the search for 'real happiness.' I can, however, remember being carried round the room on the uplifted arms of half a dozen gentlemen, in order that I might embrace a lady six feet three high.

A speciality of the period was the shadow-graph party. In the middle of a party a sheet would be hung up at one end of the room from ceiling to floor, the lights were put out except for a single bright light behind the sheet, which thus became a brilliantly illuminated screen. The shadows of two scantily clad figures, male and female, would then appear upon the screen. They made a pantomime show of meeting, kissing, quarrelling, making love. . . . They would be followed by other amorously gesticulating figures, sometimes three or more. The game was for the guests to guess who were the fellow guests whose shadows they had just been observing. There were prizes for correct guesses.

It was after one of these parties that I went with a friend, a well-known singer, to the rooms of an actor round the corner. The actor had been having a small party of his own, but it was over and only

o

two or three survivors were sitting rather drearily round a fire imbibing, of all improbable drinks, cocoa. The door leading into a darkened inner room was ajar. As we entered a deep contralto voice was heard through the aperture : 'Are those men who have just come in?' Our host answered that we were indeed men. 'Send one of them in to me,' said the voice menacingly. I looked at the singer and the singer looked at me. 'Better toss up for it,' said the actor. We tossed and I won. With a rueful grin the singer disappeared through the half-open door which then closed behind him. He was not seen again. I mention these incidents in no spirit of vainglory but merely to convey the atmosphere of the time, a time in which such names as those of Mary Butts, Bobby Heseltine, Douglas Goldring, were names to conjure with.

Many harsh things have been said about the 'Twenties. 'They were frivolous, heartless, cynical. There was no sense of responsibility and men lived only for the present. People had only one aim, to have a good time. . . .'

Possibly, possibly not.   These criticisms have, no doubt, their measure of truth, yet even if most of them be true we did, I submit, less harm in the world than the men of the frightened 'Thirties or the dreary 'Forties. But one thing, at least, was true of us, and I put it here on record. We *did* have fun ; we *did* have a good time.

Another expression of release was the cabaret. At the Cave of Harmony, in Seven Dials, Harold Scott and Elsa Lanchester, the Elsa who subsequently married Charles Laughton, were providing cabaret with a special emphasis on sea-chanties and a special slant on Victorian songs.   There was a rage for Victorian songs, sung with mocking derision—as we guyed the sentimentality of our fathers. How well I remember Elsa Lanchester rendering 'Sell No More Drink to My Father' or 'She Was Poor but She was Honest.'   I remember still better, probably because I took more delight in, her rendering of the lilting 'Ratcatcher's Daughter.'

The Cave of Harmony was succeeded by or developed into or was replaced by Ridgeway's Late Joys, which met in the early 'Thirties high up in an attic overlooking Covent Garden. Today its traditions have descended by legitimate line of inheritance to the Players' Theatre in Villiers Street, which has survived to become the popular Mecca of family parties and people up from the suburbs and the provinces for a 'good time,' thus testifying to the English genius for making anything respectable, provided only that it survives long enough.   Only Philip Godfrey with his guitar survives from an earlier dispensation, and his songs, I suspect, have been diluted to match the audiences whom he so unfailingly delights.

I hesitate to add a word on the political atmosphere of the time, lest it should seem to be infected by an even greater measure of subjectivity—this, it might be said, is a man speaking out of an experience which is wholly personal and in no sense representative—than what I have written hitherto. Nevertheless, the political atmosphere was at once so characteristic and so different from what was to follow that I cannot resist the temptation to speak of it, as I remember it.

It was a time, then, of political optimism and innocent hope. To those of us who were on the Left—and everybody I knew was on the Left—everything seemed possible both for ourselves and for the nation. The coming in 1924 of the first Labour Government, albeit a minority Government, was for us an occasion of surprise no less than of triumphant delight. Under it and its successors Socialism would be introduced, private property abolished, class barriers broken down and the millenium established. What was more, in these delightful developments we were to play a leading part. For this pre-eminently was *our* Government. In common with most of my friends, I was personally acquainted with many of the newly elected Labour M.P.s. At the 1917 Club in Gerrard Street, which set the political tone of our group and period, Charles Trevelyan, Jimmy Maxton, even Ramsay MacDonald himself could be seen lunching—seen and talked to. Most of us belonged to the I.L.P., then in the heydey of its influence, attended its Easter Conferences and caballed vigorously behind the scenes.

It was a period of political week-ends. Groups of us would gather at some guest house or holiday camp where we would read papers to one another on the basis of taxation in a Socialist State or vigorously debate the issue of compensation v. confiscation. I used to gather parties of students for week-ends in the country, week-ends which culminated in a week or fortnight's Summer School in August, at which we used seriously to consider what influence we, as an 'academic' group—I put 'academic' in quotes because most of us belonged only to the W.E.A.—could bring to bear upon the counsels of the Government. We were at once solemn and high-spirited. . . .

One of the outstanding political features of the time was its Pacifism. In the middle 'Twenties a spate of Pacifist books, plays and films was ushered in by Herr Remarque's *All Quiet on the Western Front*. Appalled by the slaughter of the last war, young men were everywhere proclaiming their refusal to take part in another. In the 1917 Club it was held to be a mark of glory to have gone to prison as a conscientious objector. . . . The culmination of this phase was reached in the early 'Thirties when the Oxford Resolution pledging young men not to fight for their King and Country was carried by a large majority, to be followed by similar resolutions, similarly carried, in almost every University in the country.

Looking forward, as we did, to a better future, it was inevitable that we should devote special attention to our children. I doubt whether there was ever a time in which young parents, both potential and actual, devoted so much thought and energy to a consideration of the right way to bring up children. Under the influence of psycho-analysis, we were on one point agreed, namely, the awful importance of the early years and, therefore, of parenthood. From the way we talked, you would think that nobody had ever had children before. That the inhibitions and prohibitions of the Victorian age were deplorable we were also agreed. Children were experiments with rights of their own, including the right to develop in their own way. Interminably we argued the great question at what point, if any, was the right to self-expression, to be denied. Was a child, for example, to run up and down on the keys of the grand piano? A body of doctrine called 'The New Education' grew up, and schools were founded to give it concrete expression. A. S. Neill, Curry, and Bertrand Russell were great names among us as we eagerly discussed the rival merits of Summerhill, Dartington Hall and Beacon Hill schools.

Our children, we were convinced, would grow up into a generation of fearless, uninhibited, guilt-free, complex-free adults. A couple of decades later they had, in fact, grown up and appeared as the young men and women of the late 'Forties, as, in fact, the generation we see around us today. Are they, then, by and large any better than we were, are they, indeed, any different, or have the educational and political hopes of the 'Twenties faded with their gaiety? The answer, I am afraid, is all too plain.

In restrospect, the 'Twenties stand revealed as the last gleam of the civilization that received its death-blow in 1914, a gleam that flickered uncertainly for a few happy, hectic years until, in the storms and stresses of the 'Thirties, the candle guttered and went out.

So much for the Nineteen-twenties. Suppose we now turn back a hundred years and read some pages from a diary written by a young lady of fashion in the Eighteen-twenties. She lived, as it happens, in Stratford Place, where THE SATURDAY BOOK *is published.*

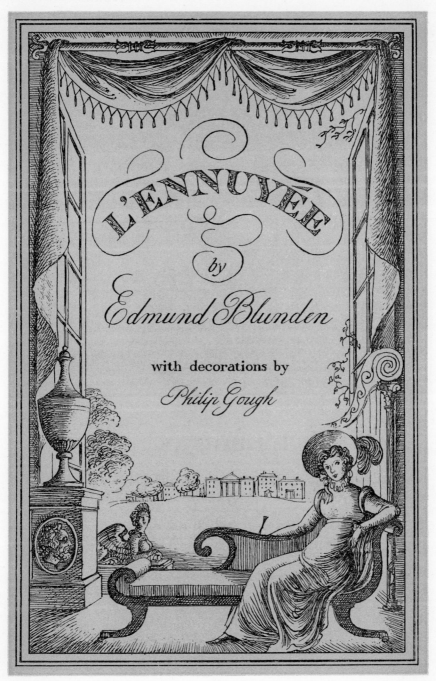

L'ENNUYÉE

by

Edmund Blunden

with decorations by

Philip Gough

L'Ennuyée

by *EDMUND BLUNDEN*

MISS GEORGINA BEET, if this conjecture of her name is correct, would not have been altogether pleased to find her journal being read by anyone without a title. Still, that one notebook, rescued by me from a street bookstall, is perhaps all that now survives of her personality, and she was eager to impress her personality in one way or another on a careless world. It was almost all that she could find to do, using the technique to which she had been confined. With a touch of broad humour added, and less of the anxious chase of the eligible male, young Georgina might have left a brilliant picture of the West End in her young days.

The volume which conveys this hint in some of its pages is not all diary. At one end of it the writer practises her Italian upon the 'Storia delle Stornello' and other subjects ; and she finds room for a little score-sheet which reads thus, '1824 — London. 45 Balls. 17 Partys. 14 Dinners. 18 Operas.' But at the other end a considerable number of daily happenings is recorded in a thin and impatient handwriting, beginning with the address 'Stratford Place, March 16th, 1822.' In the main I shall let this fashionable girl speak for herself, an exercise which will not really vex her very seriously.

'*Saturday*. I have at last determined to write a journal and there-fore without further preface shall proceed to state the placidity of my temper was a little ruffled by being *ordered* (how I hate the word) to take a walk with Mama in the Park consequently Music and Drawing were neglected for the day—Rather agreeably surprised by a Visit from one of our Scottish friends, young Graham of Mosmore, and invited him to accompany us to the Benyons Ball on Monday. In the Evening we went with the Fylers and their vulgar-looking French Governess to see Matthews at Home, was extremely amused, and not at all tired tho' we did not return Home till past Midnight. N.B. do not approve of Governnesses being brought into Public.

'*Sunday*. A damp gloomy morning. Mrs. David could not give us seats at Church, as her family are in Town we therefore read our Prayers at Home—I never felt more inclined to be idle than I did the whole après midi, and opened first one Book and then another in the vain hope of finding something to fix my wandering imagination. A visit from *Crusoe* did not enliven us much, and it was with real pleasure I hailed a beam of sunshine which enabled us to take our drive in the Park, after having been detained near $\frac{1}{2}$ an hour by Mr Talbot who came to make excuses for his non-appearance at our Quadrille which were graciously received——

'*Monday* 18th. Did not move out of the house the whole day, consequently it passed in the usual routine of Drawing and Music, my Magdalene improves daily, I certainly feel a slight sentiment of vanity when I look at her beauteous face, and inwardly pray that my fondness for Drawing may stand the test of years, and that when the gay Visions of Youth fade before the cooler eye of age, it may beguile some tedious hours away, and when the amusements of the world have lost their attractions it may with Music enable me to be contented at home (where ere that Home may lie). But to return to the present time, we made our appearance at Mr Benyons at $\frac{1}{2}$ past 10, the rooms by no means full, owing to Lady Neave's Ball which unfortunately divided the Company. I danced eight Quadrilles, Vide Messrs Oakeley, Stracey, Shirley, Graham, Robbins, Walton, Reynolds, and Paul, the last certainly the most agreeable. I wish he did not live in the *Strand* (how very ridiculous). Felt in perfect good humour and pleased which is not always the case and returned home at ½ past two.'

In the next entry made by the diarist we come across a name which was once resplendent. In 1822 Herr Kalkbrenner, a native of Cassel in Germany, was at the height of his musical reputation in England, being ranked as the equal of Moscheles. 'His style of playing,' one of his contemporaries wrote, 'is peculiar, but his command of the piano is prodigious.'

'*Tuesday*. Rather fatigued with the dissipation of last night but received a Lesson from Mr Kalkbrenner with proper attention, tho' I am inclined to think his Guinea is earned too easily, however he is certainly an incomparable Master, and a very good Composer which is fortunate as he has a strange *penchant* in favor of his own Music.

'*Wednesday*. The Fylers dined with us today en famille and gave us a slight insight into their menage, not very prepossessing, indeed poor Mrs Fyler (whether from ill-health I know not) is so totally devoid of animation with such an *Asiatic* indolence of disposition, that no domestic occupation appears to interest her and I should much fear her intellectual resources are either very limited, or but seldom called into action, such a Companion during a Winters Evening's tête à tête, must naturally render his home not very agreeable to Mr F, who is apparently gifted with an excellent flow of Spirits, and tho' I should not point him out as a *sensible* Man, possesses talents sufficients to bear in *rational* [——].'

At this critical moment the Journal is interrupted; four pages have been cut out; and when we resume the diarist is proving that somebody can 'be no judge of the feelings of those, who harassed by affliction and oppressed with worldly care, look forward to the Tomb for that repose they are denied on Earth.' She proceeds normally: 'An Invitation to Dinner at Sir John Lubbock's on the 28th—We are unfortunately engaged.' The next day's notes bring in a famous R.A., Richard Cosway, who has been a neighbour of Georgina's in Stratford Place until the year before.

'*Saturday*. Mr Davis paid us a visit to communicate the death of Mr Daws with whom Papa was slightly acquainted, he has lately succeeded to a large property.—Mrs Cosway has sent us a Ticket to view the remaining works of Mr Cosway which she purposes taking abroad with her, there are many good Miniatures in the collection, and a few oil paintings not very first rate, but by far the greater proportion consists of rough sketches of etchings in the different styles of drawing, some very well designed, but in too unfinished a state to afford much amusement.

'*Sunday*. Mama suffered so much all night from a Gathering in the Thumb which totally prevented her sleeping that she was unable to go to Church, I therefore acted Chaperone to Eliza as Mrs Davis was able to give us Seats at the Trinity Chapel. We dined at Mr E. Hopkinson's, the Party tolerably agreeable, and as Miss Dutton was there I did not find it dull, was very sorry to hear Capt Ferrers who we have known for many years is deranged, brought on in a great measure by considerable losses at Play while at Cheltenham.

'*Monday*. Did not stir out of the house the whole day, and took the opportunity of dispatching a letter to Harriet Grant, which ought to have been done at least two months since. I must confess I am a very bad Correspondent, and there are so few people for whom I feel any interest, that my Epistolary talents are fortunately but seldom called into play. I am happy to say I have not the slightest tincture of Romance in my disposition, consequently am but ill adapted to be the Repository of a Young Ladies *most secret thoughts* and none I trust will ever fix upon me as a *confidential friend*.

'*Tuesday*. Received my weekly lesson from Mr Kalkbrenner: he was in high good humour having purchased (at an Auction of old furniture in the City) an original picture of Poussin's, representing the Rape of the Sabines, for two pounds which he says when cleaned will be worth a thousand—among the remarkable events of this day, that I have begun working a beautiful border for a Dress in coloured Lambswool. I will not pretend to fix a time for its termination, as I am not very expeditious and indeed have but little time.—Miss Lilly was married this morning to Mr Bunbury the rejected admirer of Miss Wilmot! Prodigious!!!

'*Wednesday*. Mama having lent the carriage to the Francklyns who are come to Town for a few days, we remained at home. I employed the greater part of the morning working at my dress which amuses me extremely as yet it has the powerful charm of novelty to recommend it, but I am quite determined to finish it myself, however ennuyant I may find it—The Elliots, Davis's, Devitts, Hopkinsons, Williamsons, Cousin William and Mr Graham dined with us, but from Miss Devitt and Mrs Hopkinson sending excuses our Party was reduced to twelve, I sat between the two Beaus but not finding Mr Devitt particularly agreeable, amused myself with talking of our friends in

Edinburgh and the many pleasant days we spent there, with Mr Graham who is perfectly unaffected and good humoured without being very lively, he tells me General Coghlin is finally rejected by the fair Lady who he had fixed upon to supply the place of his first wife, she insisted upon having the saddle Horse, which was an excess of extravagance the General never would permit, as he assured her he never had a horse in his life, it was an expense he could not afford, his income not exceeding four thousand and *thirty* pounds per annum.

'*Thursday*. We attempted to take our accustomed walk in the Park but found the day so very warm, that we were obliged to return home to pass the day in the usual routine of occupation. Mr Nisbet came to Dress my Hair at four at seven we proceeded to Mr Briscoes and never since my first appearance on the stage of Life, was I at anything so terribly dull. Mrs B was too unwell to make her appearance and the Dinner passed off with more than usual gloom. I was quite delighted when our Carriage was announced and indeed had we remained much longer I must certainly have indulged myself in a quiet Nap, however we made our appearance in Trio at Mrs Bishops Ball, in very good Spirits, at half past ten, the Rooms had attained to Pine Apple heat, without being too crowded, but the dancing certainly did not go off with Spirit. I walked through five Quadrilles, with Messrs Reynolds, Stracey, Fyler, Bowden and Robbins but I do not think I enjoyed it so much as usual. The Supper was very elegant, but it was with real pleasure I found myself comfortably in Bed.'

In this tone Georgina continues. She denied that she felt any inclination towards romance, but at a dinner party next evening it is likely that she suspected it. '*Capt Rowley*' arrived, and upon his entrance, she says, 'my eyes instinctively turned towards him, to endeavour to trace some resemblance to a distant relation of his, with whom we were intimately acquainted.' There was after all no such resemblance, but perhaps to this observer Rowley looked well enough in his own way ; for here a page has been cut out.

'*Tuesday*. Mr Kalkbrenner disappointed me this morning but comes for his Guinea tomorrow. . . .

'*Wednesday*. My Music Lesson went off with tolerable eclat after after which I sat down quietly to begin Carlo Dolci's Saviour which will make I think a beautiful Drawing. I was interrupted about twelve by Mr Talbot and as I know him of old to be an everlasting visitor I took my work and finished a Carnation while he was desiring Mama to find him a wife, and explaining the requisite qualifications. I concluded he was a fixture for the morning which would have been the

case had not Mr Robbins and Mr Carpenter made their appearance,
a short time before the Carriage was announced and being Strangers,
the *Ghost of Don Giovanni* vanished.

'*Thursday*.   Practised diligently for nearly two hours not without
a slight feeling of ennui towards the close, indeed Kalkbrenner Studies
are too much for the patience of a frail mortal like myself.   Mr Graham
paid us a Visit, I am always glad to see him, more from the agreeable
recollections he brings to my mind than from his own amiable persona
—tho' he is an agreeable matter of fact sort of person. . . .

'*Friday*. Hot cross Bunns it being good Friday. . . . I took a long
walk with Papa and visited the different Catholic Chapels but found
them all closed which induced us to take a turn in the Park. . . .

'*Saturday*.   Lord Petersham enlivened the Park by his *wonderful*
presence.   I thought it too cold to walk. . . .

'*Sunday*.   Went to Church as usual after which we paid several
visits and finding every body at Home we were too late for the Park as
we had to dress to Dine at Mrs Elliot's where we met the usual Sunday
Party, not very gay—Mr Wesley Doyle, Mr Grenfell, etc., etc.   Mrs E.

indulged us with Solos, Duetts, Trios, etc., etc. till Mama's patience was nearly exhausted and we made our escape as Mr Doyle was preparing to delight us with a *simple* Ballad of his own composition.

'*Tuesday.* Mr Kalkbrenner came to me at twelve and staid some time longer than usual owing to my having told him I was to play at Mrs Fyler's tonight where Papa dined, altho' Mama and I more than once thought of sending an excuse, which it would have been happy

for us to have done, for a more stupid Evening I never past. the only Young Ladies there were two Miss Linds neither pretty nor agreeable but so well dressed that I quite regretted seeing them set off on foot for Manchester Street tho' on reflection I thought it more probable they were bending their steps towards Piccadilly, in hopes of finding an *Agony* on the Stand.

'*Wednesday and Thursday.* Mrs Dottin and Lady Arundel Lady and Miss Hunter and the Miss Olivers were among the list of distinguished fashionables who honoured us with a visit, the only news I heard was the approaching marriage of Miss Collier and a Greek Sans sous therefore I suppose sans soucis.

'*Friday.* Mama went out notwithstanding the heavy rain for the character of a Cook, which proved most satisfactory. I remained at home as we [were] going to a Quadrille at Colonel Drinkwaters which I was sure would be dull and my fears were fully verified on entering the room and casting an anxious glance around, in the vain hope of meeting one friendly countenance, but not one appeared to bless my sight, and it was with regret I thought of the late hour at which the Carriage was ordered. I danced or rather walked two Quadrilles with young Drinkwater and a Mr Bosanquet, both perfectly uninteresting, and it was with pleasure that at any other time or place, he would not have occasioned, I hailed the appearance of Mr Dewar, a young and handsome Scotchman, but who on my first introduction I did not find *à mon gré,* however, whether from the contrast with the many very ill looking red haired Beaux who graced the Ballroom, or from his feeling a wish to be agreeable Mr Dewar raised himself greatly in my estimation and tho' there is still a certain je ne sais quoi about him, which I do not admire, he appears a lively gentlemanlike young man. We returned home at one, neither fatigued, or amused.

'*Sunday.* A foggy morning, but as it cleared a little towards eleven, we walked to Church, the Sermon particularly good, and well delivered, it was addressed to the Young, and tolerably impressive, the preacher being young himself did not paint this life in the usual gloomy colours adapted by more *reverend* divines, who enjoy the good things of this world themselves but would deny them to their Brethren. The Park was very full of indifferent Company . . .

'*Saturday.* Our Dinner at General Rebow's was very pleasant, the Party consisted of the Lennards, Birchs, Genl. Peacock, Sir T. Ormsby, and Mr W. Sperling, the last, a gay young Lancer with a fine pair of black Mustachios, was my voisin at Dinner, and was very agreeable without any affectation, we adjourned to the drawing-room, where I improved my acquaintance with Miss Rebow, a very nice lively little girl, and after playing Kalkbrenner's Rondo [one of K's numerous Rondos] to an admiring audience we took our leave and proceeded to Mrs L. Mackenzie's in Portland Place where we found a formal circle of ugly women and stupid men (nearly all strangers to us) listening (not with much attention certainly) to Sig. Torri and other professional and amateur performers, I had promised to play but most fortunately was not called upon to exhibit till the Carriage was ready and therefore to my great joy I escaped. . . .

'*Saturday*. General Peachy paid us a visit with Mr. Seymour and Capt Rattray the last remained so long that we had but just time to Dress for Mr Elliot's Dinner which I should not have been sorry to have missed, as I never was at anything more triste, the Party consisted of the Rounds, Adam's, Penfolds, Williams and Capts Hawkins and Barton of the Guards, both appeared preeminently stupid . . . the Evening was as triste as the Dinner . . .

'*Monday*. Our Friends the Andersons arrived last night. Mr A. paid us a visit this morning and we ordered the Carriage earlier than usual that we might call on his handsome wife and shew her the *Lions*, as it is the first time she has visited our gay Metropolis, we first introduced her to Mrs Gill and then after driving thro' the New St. Bond St. Pall Mall etc. we took a few turns in the Park, which was not very full, Mama who is always kinder to friends than they are to her, gave her ticket for Ebers Concert to Mrs A. and having procured one for Mr A. I called for them at eight and proceeded to the Opera Saloon, which we found tolerably full and the Concert began, with the whole of which we were much delighted, Mdme Campanese sung Di piacer in a most superior style, and little Caradori was encored in a pretty French Romance . . . at the end of the first Act we adjourned to the Tea room where I spoke to old Mrs. Lind (in pale pink satin) and Mrs R. Mitford. Mr Johnstone did me *the honour* of addressing some observations to me but there is a petit air de protection about him which I cannot bear. . . .

'*Tuesday*. Mr Kalkbrenner gave me his farewell lesson.—Papa will not dine out as his finger is very indisposed . . . I felt some little alarm at entering the Opera House alone but as the Box was situated in the centre of the Pit Tier I had but a very short distance to walk. The House was crowded to excess and owing to the Drawing room many Ladies wore their Court Plumes and Diamonds, which had a most brilliant effect particularly when the Audience stood up for the National Anthem which was sung in honour of the Birthday of the King, the Opera was Moses in Egypt called Peter the Hermit very dull and so long that we had only one Act of the Ballet which did not begin till near one. Paul and Mlle Noble made their debut and Albert took leave amidst thunders of applause. Mrs Anderson was so fatigued that she fainted which delayed us so much that we were not home till past two and Mama was so frightened that she was thinking of sending the footman in quest of us.

'*Wednesday*. . . . We arrived so late that most of the Company were gone the remainder were dancing a Quadrille to a Piano on the

Carpet. I was persuaded to walk one with Mr Talbot whose ugly face was half hid under a profusion of curls which he seemed to regard with great complacency and was delighted when Mama complimented him on his good looks, we returned home at one.

'*Friday*. After much debate it was agreed we should send our excuses to Mrs Walton's Ball this Evening. I was certainly delighted as independently of not liking the People Bedford Row is too far to go at night without having relais of Horses on the Road. — We took our Drive on the Park which I think far preferable to Almacks in the *east*, and dined at home en famille.

'*Tuesday*. . . . A Musical Party at Mrs Mayne's . . . Mr Baird honoured me with his *kind* protection to the refreshment room . . .

'*Wednesday*. Dined at the Edwards', their beautiful house being just finished and very beautiful it certainly is, I passed a very pleasant day as I sat between Mr Dickens and Mr Dewar, the latter improves wonderfully on acquaintance and is gradually becoming a great favourite, he is very different from the common herd of Dandies, who when they have told you the Park was full and empty and that London is dull have exhausted the whole content of their frizzled head.

'*Saturday*. Dined at Mr Blackwood's the dullest Party and worst dinner I ever met with I shall certainly *erase* their names from *my visiting* book.'

Some continental tours provided Miss Beet with new descriptions and disapprovals. The journal was not always kept, and when we arrive at the New Year, 1824, and her new home, 35 Harley Street, she is summing up the days more briefly than formerly. Dull dinner parties, dull music parties, sometimes she goes, sometimes she doesn't, —especially if the hostess lives '*in the East*.' Some of the regulars of 1822 are still quadrilling, but she attempts no new character studies even of Mr Dewar. On April 24, 'Went to the Opera for the first time, Mme Pasta's debut in Othello, quite delighted with the whole performance.' Against such enjoyments stupid routs and strings of people 'all insufferable, in many respect' were always to be offset. Sometimes she slips into Italian, '. . . ma non andiamo.' She had become bored at being bored, a state which once had had its uses; and is not much inclined even to record, 'We arrived at St. James', at half past two, and left without accident a little before seven the Drawing Room was unusually crowded amongst the number we recognized several acquaintances, in the evening we went to Mrs Oliver's Quadrille in Harley Street, it promised well, but I was too fatigued with the morning exertion to enjoy myself, but was persuaded to walk one Quadrille with Mr Barlow, who was desirous of exhibiting with a Lady in Court Plumes.'

On June 8, 'The Opera Tancredi most beautifully performed was obliged to leave before the Ballet as we were engaged to a *tremendous* Party at Mrs Briscoe's—twelve old women and three men, Lady Mawbey entertained us with her croaking voice, we remained about half an hour determined it should be the last we would pass in that House.' Indeed nothing was up to standard; the Wedding of Figaro was indifferently performed and Catalani disappointing; Lady Becchey's Fancy Ball was a desert; Lady Owen's was crowded and hot. The year 1825 brought no improvement and the diary became occasional and terse. 'Quadrille . . . Excuses . . . Ditto . . . dull.' The final entry, on February 17, is 'Dinner at home.' How to account for the silence afterwards I hardly know; it may be that Mr Dewar, or some less familiar figure, at last rescued Georgina from her doldrums, but one day the rest of her story may come to light. So far as she had got by 1825 she is all too like the over-trained and under-trained beauties whom Shelley stigmatized a few years previously in 'Peter Bell,' as courteous, cruel and inhuman. But I wish I could get a view of her at last as a rejoicing bride, not without wit.

THE END OF THE TWELFTH VOLUME OF THE
SATURDAY BOOK

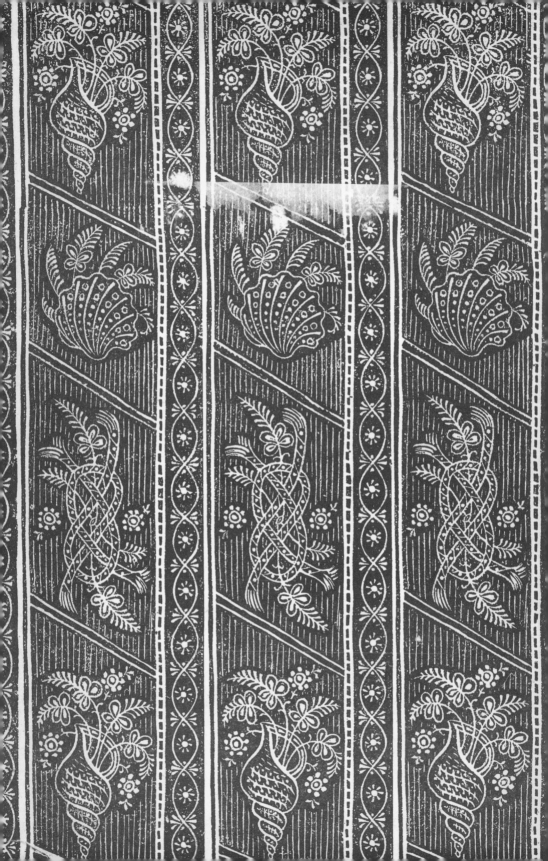